# WHEN YOUR ARTISTRY CAPTURES THE UNKNOWN, YOU'VE MADE HISTORY.

This watch is a witness to insatiable curiosity, and incredible underwater photography. Worn by an artist who reveals the mysteries of the ocean. It doesn't just tell time. It tells history.

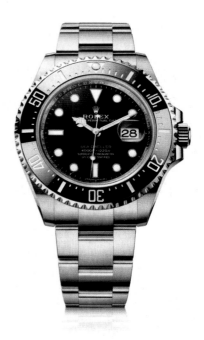

OYSTER PERPETUAL SEA-DWELLER

D1492783

ROLEX

# CONTENTS

SEPTEMBER 2017 • VOL. 232 • NO. 3 • OFFICIAL JOURNAL OF THE NATIONAL GEOGRAPHIC SOCIETY

## FRONT

## FEATURES

NAT GEO WILD

## WALK ON *CHINA'S WILD SIDE*

Very different wildlife ecosystems exist in two regions of China. The high-altitude Tibet Autonomous Region is populated by animals that can tolerate thin air, like the wild yak. The Yunnan region is a subtropical paradise, home to the only elephants in the nation, including this baby Asian elephant in Xishuangbanna Wild Elephant Valley (right). Explore both regions in the two-part series *China's Wild Side,* airing September 1 and September 8 at 9/8c on Nat Geo WILD.

TELEVISION

### SEE CASSINI'S FINAL VIEW OF SATURN

When NASA's Cassini spacecraft plunges into Saturn this month, it will be the final act in an unprecedented 20-year mission of discovery. Trace the probe's epic journey in *Mission Saturn,* airing September 15 at 9/8c on National Geographic.

BOOKS

### HOW 'WONDER DRUGS' CHANGED CHICKEN

Chicken is a staple of diets worldwide, yet many consumers know little about the use of antibiotics in poultry production. Journalist Maryn McKenna reveals the role that these drugs play in industrial farming in *Big Chicken,* available at *shopng.com/books* and wherever books are sold.

BIG CHICKEN

The Incredible Story of How Antibiotics Created Modern Agriculture and Changed the Way the World Eats

*Author of Superbug*

MARYN MCKENNA

BOOKS

### STUNNING MAPS, IMAGES FILL ATLAS

Reimagined and updated, National Geographic's *Visual Atlas of the World, 2nd Edition,* is 416 pages of breathtaking photography and state-of-the-art cartography. The atlas goes on sale September 19 at *shopng.com/books* and wherever books are sold.

**Subscriptions** For subscriptions or changes of address, contact Customer Service at *ngmservice.com* or call 1-800-647-5463. Outside the U.S. or Canada call +1-813-979-6845. We occasionally make our subscriber names available to companies whose products or services might be of interest to you. If you prefer not to be included, you may request that your name be removed from promotion lists by calling 1-800-NGS-LINE (647-5463). To opt out of future direct mail from other organizations, visit *DMAchoice.org,* or mail a request to: DMA Choice, c/o Data & Marketing Association, P.O. Box 643, Carmel, NY 10512.

NATIONAL GEOGRAPHIC (ISSN 0027-9358) PUBLISHED MONTHLY BY NATIONAL GEOGRAPHIC PARTNERS, LLC, 1145 17TH ST. NW, WASHINGTON, DC 20036. ONE YEAR MEMBERSHIP: $39.00 U.S. DELIVERY, $44.00 TO CANADA, $51.00 TO INTERNATIONAL ADDRESSES. SINGLE ISSUE: $7.00 U.S. DELIVERY, $10.00 CANADA, $15.00 INTERNATIONAL. (ALL PRICES IN U.S. FUNDS; INCLUDES SHIPPING AND HANDLING.) PERIODICALS POSTAGE PAID AT WASHINGTON, DC, AND ADDITIONAL MAILING OFFICES. POSTMASTER: SEND ADDRESS CHANGES TO NATIONAL GEOGRAPHIC, P.O. BOX 62130, TAMPA, FL 33662. IN CANADA, AGREEMENT NUMBER 40063649, RETURN UNDELIVERABLE ADDRESSES TO NATIONAL GEOGRAPHIC, P.O. BOX 4412, STN. A, TORONTO, ONTARIO M5W 3W2. UNITED KINGDOM NEWSSTAND PRICE £5.99. REPR. EN FRANCE: EMD FRANCE SA, BP 1029, 59011 LILLE CEDEX; TEL. 320.300.302; CPPAP 0715U89037; DIRECTEUR PUBLICATION: D. TASSINARI DIR. RESP. ITALY; RAPP IMD SRL, VIA G. DA VELATE 11, 20162 MILANO; AUT. TRIB. MI 258 26/5/84 POSTE ITALIANE SPA; SPED. ABB. POST. DL 353/2003 (CONV L.27/02/2004 N.46) ART 1 C. 1 DCB MILANO STAMPA QUAD/GRAPHICS, MARTINSBURG, WV 25401. MEMBERS: IF THE POSTAL SERVICE ALERTS US THAT YOUR MAGAZINE IS UNDELIVERABLE, WE HAVE NO FURTHER OBLIGATION UNLESS WE RECEIVE A CORRECTED ADDRESS WITHIN TWO YEARS.

PHOTO: JOSHUA CHENG, NHNZ

# NEW INSIGHTS INTO ADDICTION

Every 25 minutes in the United States, a baby is born addicted to opioids.

That heartbreaking statistic is but one symptom of an epidemic that shows no sign of abating. The 33,000 overdose deaths from opioids in 2015 were a 16 percent rise over the previous year, which also set a record. Drug overdoses are now a leading cause of death among Americans under 50—but only part of a broader addiction landscape that ranges from drug and alcohol abuse to obsessive eating, gambling, and even sex.

For this month's cover story, "The Addicted Brain," we went in search of the "why." Why do human beings get addicted to substances and behaviors we know will harm us? What can new research tell us about addiction and the brain? Most important: Can what we're learning help more people recover?

"Not long ago the idea of repairing the brain's wiring to fight addiction would have seemed far-fetched," medical writer Fran Smith reports in our story. "But advances in neuroscience have upended conventional notions about addiction—what it is, what can trigger it, and why quitting is so tough."

The very nature of addiction is being rethought. In 2016, when he was U.S. surgeon general, Vivek Murthy—who's interviewed in this issue—affirmed what scientists had contended for years, as Smith says: "Addiction is a disease, not a moral failing. It's characterized not necessarily by dependence or withdrawal but by compulsive repetition of an activity despite life-damaging consequences. This view has led many scientists to accept the once heretical idea that addiction is possible without drugs."

Still, drug abuse takes a huge toll nationwide: nearly $200 billion a year in costs related to health, crime, and lost productivity. Nowhere does this play out more starkly than in West Virginia,

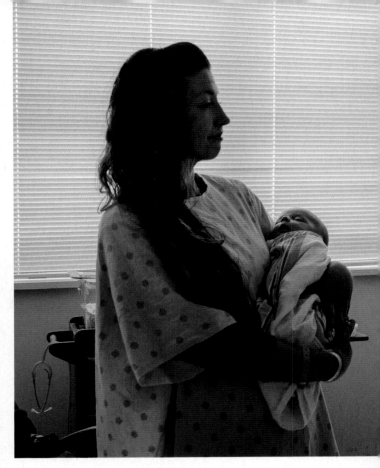

which owns what Senator Shelley Moore Capito calls an "unfortunate distinction": the nation's highest rate of drug overdose deaths.

A native West Virginian elected to the Senate in 2014, Capito sees the issue in personal terms. "The most heart-wrenching part is that it hits everybody ... I've been in meetings where they tell you to look to the right or the left and say, 'That's what a heroin addict looks like.'"

What she's learned, she says, is that turning the corner will require a spectrum of solutions—everything from more support at the state and federal levels for treatment and prevention programs to more facilities like Lily's Place, a Huntington, West Virginia, medical center for babies born dependent on drugs.

Seeing the suffering, Capito says, "I've learned not to be quite so judgmental."

Thank you for reading *National Geographic.*

*[signature]*

Susan Goldberg, *Editor in Chief*

At Cabell Huntington Hospital in Huntington, West Virginia, Jordann Thomas, 28, holds her five-week-old son, who was born with neonatal abstinence syndrome (NAS), a state of opiate withdrawal. Thomas, who's in recovery from heroin addiction, says she became pregnant while using a withdrawal support drug that crossed the placenta and caused her baby's NAS. The syndrome has become so common that the hospital's ward devoted to it often has more infant patients than beds.

WHAT WILL THE FUTURE LOOK LIKE?

# YEAR MILLION

BRAND NEW SERIES
**STARTS SEPTEMBER**

NATIONAL
GEOGRAPHIC

SKY   VIRGIN MEDIA   BT   TALKTALK

natgeotv.com/uk

# WHAT IT MEANS TO BE HEALTHY

As U.S. surgeon general from 2014 until spring 2017, **Vivek Murthy,** 40, extended his office's public health advocacy to matters such as reliable transportation, safe neighborhoods, and affordable housing. Today he continues to stress the need to reduce stigmas around mental illness and to promote emotional well-being and healthy habits.

**'WE NEED TO CHANGE HOW WE THINK ABOUT EMOTIONS.'**
VIVEK MURTHY, FORMER U.S. SURGEON GENERAL

**You say emotional well-being is just as important as eating a healthy diet and staying active. Why?**
When I began my tenure as surgeon general, I did not intend to focus on emotional well-being. But it became a priority after I traveled the country listening to people in small towns and big cities. What I sensed was that people were experiencing a high degree of emotional pain. I think of emotional well-being as a resource within each of us that allows us to do more and to perform better. That doesn't mean just the absence of mental illness. It's the presence of positive emotions that allows us to be resilient in the face of adversity.

**How do we fix that?**
The first thing is that we need to change how we think about emotions. Emotions are a source of power, and that's what science tells us. But many people I encounter have been led to think of emotions as a source of weakness. The second thing we have to do is cultivate emotional well-being. There are tools, and they're relatively simple. They include sleep, physical activity, contemplative practices like gratitude and meditation, and social connection as well.

**In today's news you can see a lot of stress, people burned out. What does that tell you as a physician?**
I am deeply concerned about the level of stress that our country is experiencing. I think it's preventing us from achieving our full potential. I have long believed that there are fundamentally two forces or emotions that drive our decisions—love and fear. Love has its many manifestations: compassion, gratitude, kindness, and joy. Fear often manifests in cynicism, anger, jealousy, and anxiety. I worry that many of our communities are being driven by fear. It's partly because of the things we read about in the news that give us pause about the state of the world. And it's also because we haven't really prioritized cultivating positive emotions that emanate from love.

PHOTO: MARTIN SCHOELLER
THIS INTERVIEW WAS EDITED FOR LENGTH AND CLARITY.

VISIONS

**Mexico**
Dead monarch butterflies carpet a snowy forest floor in Michoacán state. At least nine million, over 40 percent of this colony, died after an unusually intense spring storm – possibly due to climate change – hit their mountain sanctuary.

**Order prints** of select *National Geographic* photos online at NationalGeographicArt.com.

PHOTO: JAIME ROJO

# #NATGEOHEALTH

**CHALLENGE** We asked the Your Shot community to show what it means to be healthy – physically, mentally, spiritually, or all of the above.

**Lance McMillan**
*Toronto, Ontario*

McMillan went to Cuba to gauge the country's economic change. In Havana he visited the Rafael Trejo boxing gym. When he saw this man run up bleachers, he set up his camera. "I waited for the moment when he would appear between the seats," McMillan says.

# I WHAT A FIND

## NATIONAL GEOGRAPHIC

# UNIQUE LODGES
# OF THE WORLD

A COLLECTION OF HANDPICKED LODGES
WHERE SUSTAINABILITY MEETS SPLENDOR

Let us plan your dream trip.
Visit natgeolodges.com or call +1-312-940-7404.

Photo: Jicaro Island Lodge, Nicaragua

The pungent sulfur compounds in cabbage appear to give it cancer-fighting properties.

DHA—a type of omega-3 fatty acid found in fish oil—boosts brain power.

Nuts are known to reduce risk of cancer, heart disease, and stroke.

## EAT, DRINK, AND BE WARY

By Catherine Zuckerman

If only it were as simple as "An apple a day keeps the doctor away." Nutrition scientists are in fact constantly scrutinizing the health properties of foods. Everything on this page, along with olive oil and tea, has been the subject of more than 20 studies in the past 25 years, says physician Michael Roizen, chief wellness officer at the Cleveland Clinic. Why? "They either have unexpected benefits," he says, "or are commonly consumed but may have risks."

Some foods—like pomegranates and pistachios in the U.S.—rise to nutrition fame because a large company that dominates the production and sales pays for much of the research. But sponsored studies can shade the science, says Roizen. The National Dairy Council, for instance, "has a huge marketing arm," allowing it to widely promote the genuinely nutritious aspects of milk, yogurt, cheese, and more. Some dairy products contain a compound called lecithin, long considered healthy. However, it interacts with gut bacteria to produce the damaging compound trimethylamine, which causes inflammation and can lead to disease. Egg yolks also have lecithin in them, so Roizen advises minimal intake.

Highly studied foods are not always the ones you should eat. Roizen suggests avoiding low-carb diets that emphasize butter, cheese, and lots of meat. Even healthy-sounding grass-fed beef contains carnitine, another trimethylamine producer. "The protein is not different whether it's grass-fed or grain-fed." Red wine or a generous splash of unadulterated extra-virgin olive oil—two top-studied foods—can slightly mitigate the negative effects of meat and dairy. But alcohol is hazardous, and olive oil is high in calories.

The best bet, says Roizen, is to follow science, not sensation. Eat vegetables. Instead of meat, choose salmon or ocean trout—they have more good fish oil than most other high-fat, low-mercury species. Drink black coffee (it can be good for the liver). Snack on nuts, but not too many. And for dessert: a bite of dark chocolate.

One glass of red wine daily is considered healthy and thought to benefit the heart.

While pomegranates and their juice are high in antioxidants, the fruit is not a panacea.

The lecithin in cheese can contribute to arterial inflammation.

Red meat contains carnitine, which may lead to cardiovascular dysfunction.

Full of beneficial, potentially disease-fighting flavonoids, dark chocolate gets top health marks.

Spices may help regulate blood pressure. Data on Indian diets suggest turmeric might help ward off Alzheimer's.

When it comes to cauliflower and other cruciferous vegetables, more is typically better.

Leafy greens like bok choy are loaded with antioxidants and magnesium, which help fight against type 2 diabetes.

# LIP-READING

By Catherine Zuckerman

Fingerprints are so last century. The new frontier? Lip prints. Like the grooves on human fingertips, the grooves on human lips are formed at the embryonic stage and are thought to remain fixed throughout life. While lip prints aren't typically used in forensics to nail criminals, they can offer clues to a person's health—particularly his or her genetic predisposition to cleft lip or palate, some of the most common birth defects.

At University of Pittsburgh's Center for Craniofacial and Dental Genetics, director Mary Marazita and geneticist Katherine Neiswanger have been studying the genetic underpinnings of cleft lip and cleft palate for more than 20 years. Recently they turned their attention to facial features, including lip patterns, to determine if certain physical traits might in some way be connected.

No single classification system exists, says Neiswanger, but lip prints tend to fall into a few categories: straight vertical lines, "branches" that spread across the lips like tree roots, crosshatches, and circular whorls. Of these, whorls—particularly when present on the lower lip—appear to be linked to a likelihood of carrying genes for clefts and other orofacial disorders, which make it difficult for babies to breastfeed and are often stigmatizing.

The field of studying lip patterns is still new, says Neiswanger, which is why a firm connection with orofacial disorders has yet to be made. But as technology improves, this research could one day lead to early diagnosis, possibly in utero. Marazita and Neiswanger believe that, in addition to lip prints, other traits—including the shape of a face or even speech characteristics—could indicate an underlying genetic vulnerability to certain disorders. "The picture is just starting to come together," says Neiswanger, "and it's very exciting."

The patterns on a person's lips might be genetically linked to clefts and other orofacial disorders. A repaired cleft lip (top) shows a whorled pattern; a non-cleft lip (above) reveals a vertical line pattern.

IMAGES: MARY L. MARAZITA, CENTER FOR CRANIOFACIAL AND DENTAL GENETICS, UNIVERSITY OF PITTSBURGH

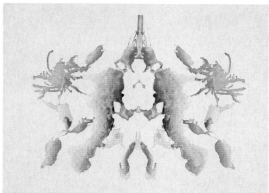 

# PICTURES OF MENTAL HEALTH

By Nina Strochlic

In a small town in Switzerland in 1917, psychiatrist Hermann Rorschach began carefully splattering paint on cards to study how the mind works. Asking people what they saw, he observed a correlation in responses from patients with schizophrenia and theorized that mental health could be assessed by how someone processes visual information.

Rorschach's original 10 images were published in 1921, the year before his death. After being brought to Chicago, they spread quickly across the United States as a popular personality test. In the second half of the century, trends like Freudian analysis fell out of favor, and the test became a synonym for pseudoscience. Critics called for a moratorium on its use. But a major 2013 study published by the American Psychological Association found it more effective than previously believed in diagnosing mental illness.

The Rorschach cards and the order in which they're presented to patients have never changed. To preserve their utility as a diagnostic tool, psychologists don't want them shown outside a clinical setting. That's a challenge Damion Searls faced as he wrote *The Inkblots*, the first biography of Rorschach. He chose to publish a few, as we are doing here. (To learn what the four inkblots above might reveal, see the next page.)

Regardless of the scientific debate, the Rorschach test has left its mark on American culture. The 10 blots are probably the "most analyzed paintings of the 20th century," says Searls.

The open-ended style of Rorschach's test became controversial in the 1960s. "People don't understand it's about *how* you see, not *what* you see," says Searls.

PHOTOS: MARK THIESSEN, NGM STAFF. RORSCHACH TEST CARDS COURTESY MERIT, L.A.

# A WEED THAT BUSTS BACTERIA

By A. R. Williams

The Brazilian pepper tree, an invasive plant in the southern United States, is showing great potential in the fight against antibiotic-resistant bacterial infections. A team of scientists studied historical accounts of its use in traditional South American medicine from as early as 1648. Focusing their experiments on its fruits, which reportedly were used to treat wounds, they then produced an extract that's able to disarm a virulent type of *Staphylococcus* bacterium.

Modern antibiotics are designed to kill bacteria. But some bacterial cells survive and pass on their resistance to their offspring, making it increasingly difficult for physicians to fight tenacious infections that threaten their patients' lives. The Brazilian pepper tree extract deploys an unconventional tactic against infections. It prevents bacterial cells from communicating, which keeps them from ganging up to create tissue-destroying toxins. That, in turn, gives the body's immune system a chance to mount its own defense against the bacteria. "This is a completely different zigzag approach to going after these really bad bugs," says Cassandra Quave, an ethnobotanist at Emory University. "It's a whole new way of thinking about how to address infections."

Quave's goal is to move such discoveries into mainstream medicine. She now plans to incorporate the extract

into a topical cream that could be used—after clinical trials—to combat chronic wounds, eczema rashes involving staph bacteria, and other skin ailments. She and her team are also investigating other parts of the pepper tree that folk healers have used to treat an array of ills, including rheumatic pains, fevers, burns, nail infections, and diarrhea.

This pressed, dried cutting from a Brazilian pepper tree is part of the Emory University Herbarium's collection of plant specimens.

## SPOILER ALERT: INKBLOT IDENTITIES

Rorschach's test (from previous page) is meant to reveal how a person processes information. There are no wrong answers, but responses that are very unusual are thought to reflect possible psychological issues. Common imagery seen in the blots, clockwise from upper left: a bat, two four-legged animals, two waiters bowing, crabs or spiders. —NS

TOP PHOTO: THARANGA SAMARAKOON, EMORY UNIVERSITY HERBARIUM

# REWIRING THE SENSE OF TOUCH

By Eve Conant

One man, one robotic arm, dozens of electrodes—these are the elements of a breakthrough experiment that's restoring the sense of touch to a paralyzed man.

Scientists have long known that the brain retains the sense of an amputated or paralyzed limb. "The brain continues to have the capacity to do what it always did," says bioengineer Robert Gaunt. "Even after injury." That's why researchers have recently been able to help people control robotic limbs with their minds.

Gaunt and his colleagues at the University of Pittsburgh and the University of Pittsburgh Medical Center aim to go even further. They're experimenting with ways to make a robotic limb "embodied," as Gaunt puts it—to make it actually feel like a part of the body and not just a tool.

Nathan Copeland, mostly paralyzed from the chest down in a car accident in his teens, participated in the experiment. The team implanted tiny sensors in his brain—in the motor cortex, which controls voluntary movement, and in the part of the sensory cortex that processes feeling in the hand. The robotic arm is then wired to send and receive signals from those sensors.

Now 31, Copeland can identify—with 84.3 percent accuracy and while blindfolded—which of his arm's prosthetic fingers are being pressed, findings reported in *Science Translational Medicine.* Copeland says he's also felt warmth and tingling sensations in the robot fingers, making him "happy, relieved, and hopeful."

The end goal, says Gaunt, is a simple one: to develop technologies so that paralysis and limb loss are "not a disability."

The Johns Hopkins Applied Physics Laboratory created this modular prosthetic limb and the one used in the Pittsburgh experiment. Both have more than 100 sensors.

# ARTIFICIAL WOMB FOR PREEMIES?

By Erika Engelhaupt

One day in the not-too-distant future, the nervous parents of a premature baby might find themselves peering into something a bit like an aquarium. Inside an artificial womb, a preemie would be submerged in simulated amniotic fluid, which would fill the lungs and give them time to develop the ability to breathe air.

A typical human pregnancy lasts about 40 weeks, and babies are considered premature at 37 weeks. Each year about 15 million babies worldwide are born prematurely—more than one-tenth of all births. The very youngest considered viable—just 22 to 23 weeks old—typically weigh only about a pound and have less than a 50 percent chance of survival. One of the main reasons they die is that their lungs are too fragile to breathe air.

In April researchers at Children's Hospital of Philadelphia reported in *Nature Communications* that they had tested an artificial womb on eight premature lambs, chosen because lambs' lungs develop similarly to those of humans. Each lamb grew in a bag filled with artificial amniotic fluid, and the beating of its heart pumped blood through its umbilical cord into a machine that acted like a placenta, adding oxygen and removing carbon dioxide.

The team reports that the lambs' lungs and other organs developed as though they were in a real sheep's womb, an

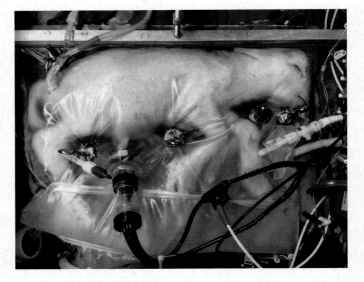

important improvement over methods used to keep preemies alive today. A few of the lambs have since grown to adulthood, and one is now more than a year old and appears normal in every way, including in its brain development.

"We don't have an intelligence test for lambs," study leader Alan Flake said at a news conference, "but we think they're pretty smart lambs."

The goal of artificial wombs, Flake says, is not to grow babies entirely outside their mothers or even to extend the limits of viability to earlier ages. Instead researchers hope for better survival and health for babies born before the critical 28-week age when their lungs are ready to take that first breath.

During the 28 days that a premature lamb grew in an artificial womb, it was able to move, open its eyes, and grow wool.

## A BETTER TEST FOR EBOLA

The Ebola virus killed more than 11,000 people in West Africa after a 2014 outbreak. Since then biochemist Mehmet Yigit, of the University at Albany, in New York, has devised a new, low-cost test that detects biomarkers of the contagious disease in urine. A sample that turns red after testing means infection. Purple means all clear. Other tests take days to yield results; Yigit's can reveal Ebola indicators within hours. —*Catherine Zuckerman*

PHOTOS: *NATURE COMMUNICATIONS* (LAMB); CARLO DE JESUS, UNIVERSITY AT ALBANY (VIALS)

# FISH'S FECUNDITY A BOON TO LABS

By Patricia Edmonds

For a creature that's less than one and a half inches long, the zebrafish *(Danio rerio)* looms large in biomedical research.

The zebrafish is a good research stand-in for its fellow vertebrate, the human, because the two have many parts in common: brain, heart, liver, kidneys. And genome sequencing has shown that 84 percent of the genes that cause disease in humans are also found in zebrafish.

Since University of Queensland cell biologist Ben Hogan began studying zebrafish in 2001, their use in labs has soared, he says. One of the fish's advantages is clear—literally. Because embryos are transparent and develop outside the mother's body, scientists can manipulate genes to model human diseases and directly observe disease changes in live animals—something not possible in another common lab animal, mice.

Though mature zebrafish are striped, young ones are see-through enough that scientists can study vascular and other systems by introducing fluorescence (right). In the brain, Hogan has found unexpected "scavenger cells" clearing away waste. If such cells occur in humans and could be controlled, they might be useful against dementia and stroke, he says.

Running repeated experiments takes lots of test subjects, and zebrafish oblige. In the wild, sunrise triggers mating; in Hogan's lab, it's spurred when he turns on lights and lifts the tank divider between the sexes. Aroused by the male's mating dance, the female spawns—as many as 300 eggs, which the male fertilizes by releasing sperm into the water. Weekly breeding ensures the embryo supply.

So far zebrafish studies have yielded insights into cancer, diabetes, muscle diseases, and more. Elizabeth Burke, a researcher at the National Institutes of Health, predicts that "these little striped swimmers have great potential for advancing medical research in the future."

## ZEBRAFISH

**HABITAT/RANGE**
Freshwater rivers and streams in South Asia

**CONSERVATION STATUS**
Least concern

**OTHER FACTS**
Zebrafish embryos absorb drugs added to the water they're in. They've been used so successfully to discover possible new drugs that several zebrafish-tested cancer drugs have now entered clinical trials.

PHOTO: STITCHED CONFOCAL MICROSCOPE IMAGE BY NEIL BOWER, INSTITUTE FOR MOLECULAR BIOSCIENCE, UNIVERSITY OF QUEENSLAND, AUSTRALIA

Addiction hijacks the brain's neural pathways. Scientists are challenging the view that it's a moral failing and researching treatments that could offer an exit from the cycle of desire, bingeing, and withdrawal that traps tens of millions of people. Janna Raine became addicted to heroin two decades ago after taking prescription pain pills for a work injury. Last year she was living in a homeless encampment under a Seattle freeway.

# THE
# ADDICTED
# BRAIN

*We're learning more about the craving that fuels self-defeating habits— and how science could help fight it.*

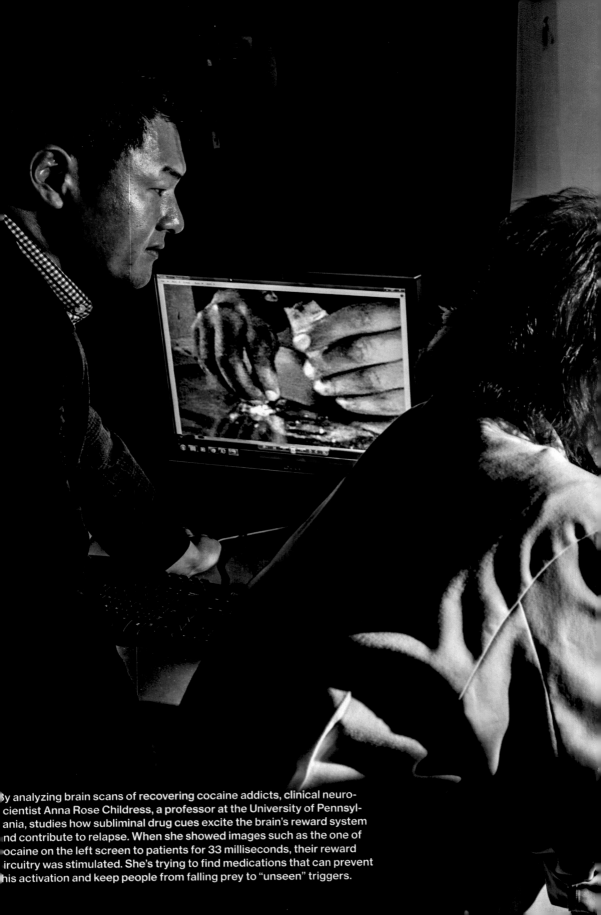

By analyzing brain scans of recovering cocaine addicts, clinical neuroscientist Anna Rose Childress, a professor at the University of Pennsylvania, studies how subliminal drug cues excite the brain's reward system and contribute to relapse. When she showed images such as the one of cocaine on the left screen to patients for 33 milliseconds, their reward circuitry was stimulated. She's trying to find medications that can prevent this activation and keep people from falling prey to "unseen" triggers.

*By Fran Smith*
*Photographs by Max Aguilera-Hellweg*

Patrick Perotti scoffed when his mother told him about a doctor who uses electromagnetic waves to treat drug addiction. "I thought he was a swindler," Perotti says.

Perotti, who is 38 and lives in Genoa, Italy, began snorting cocaine at 17, a rich kid who loved to party. His indulgence gradually turned into a daily habit and then an all-consuming compulsion. He fell in love, had a son, and opened a restaurant. Under the weight of his addiction, his family and business eventually collapsed.

He did a three-month stint in rehab and relapsed 36 hours after he left. He spent eight months in another program, but the day he returned home, he saw his dealer and got high. "I began to use cocaine with rage," he says. "I became paranoid, obsessed, crazy. I could not see any way to stop."

When his mother pressed him to call the doctor, Perotti gave in. He learned he would just have to sit in a chair like a dentist's and let the doctor, Luigi Gallimberti, hold a device near the left side of his head, on the theory it would suppress his hunger for cocaine. "It was either the cliff or Dr. Gallimberti," he recalls.

Gallimberti, a gray-haired, bespectacled psychiatrist and toxicologist who has treated addiction for 30 years, runs a clinic in Padua. His decision to try the technique, called transcranial magnetic stimulation (TMS), stemmed from dramatic advances in the science of addiction—and from his frustration with traditional treatments. Medications can help people quit drinking, smoking, or using heroin, but relapse is common, and there's no effective medical remedy for addiction to stimulants like cocaine. "It's very, very difficult to treat these patients," he says.

More than 200,000 people worldwide die every year from drug overdoses and drug-related illnesses, such as HIV, according to the United Nations Office on Drugs and Crime, and far more die from smoking and drinking. More than a billion people smoke, and tobacco is implicated in

## BREAKING THE CHAIN

**A serious cocaine addict who'd relapsed several times after treatment, Patrick Perotti finally resorted to an experimental treatment – the application of electromagnetic pulses to his prefrontal cortex – at a clinic in Padua, Italy. It worked. Psychiatrist Luigi Gallimberti has used transcranial magnetic stimulation on other patients with similar success. He and his colleagues are planning a large-scale trial. The technique is now being tested for other types of addiction by researchers around the world.**

the top five causes of death: heart disease, stroke, respiratory infections, chronic obstructive pulmonary disease, and lung cancer. Nearly one of every 20 adults worldwide is addicted to alcohol. No one has yet counted people hooked on gambling and other compulsive activities gaining recognition as addictions.

In the United States an epidemic of opioid addiction continues to get worse. The Centers for Disease Control and Prevention reported a record 33,091 overdose deaths in 2015 from opioids, including prescription painkillers and heroin—16 percent more than the previous record, set just the year before. In response to the crisis, the first ever U.S. surgeon general's report on addiction was released in November 2016. It concluded that 21 million Americans have a drug or alcohol addiction, making the disorder more common than cancer.

After spending decades probing the brains of drug-loving lab animals and scanning the brains of human volunteers, scientists have developed a detailed picture of how addiction disrupts pathways and processes that underlie desire, habit formation, pleasure, learning, emotional regulation, and cognition. Addiction causes hundreds of changes in brain anatomy, chemistry, and cell-to-cell signaling, including in the gaps between neurons called synapses, which are the molecular machinery for learning. By taking advantage of the brain's marvelous plasticity, addiction remolds neural circuits to assign supreme value to cocaine or heroin or gin, at the expense of other interests such as health, work, family, or life itself.

"In a sense, addiction is a pathological form of learning," says Antonello Bonci, a neurologist at the National Institute on Drug Abuse.

GALLIMBERTI WAS FASCINATED when he read a newspaper article about experiments by Bonci and his colleagues at NIDA and the University of California, San Francisco. They had measured electrical activity in neurons in cocaine-seeking rats and discovered that a region of the brain involved in inhibiting behavior was abnormally quiet. Using optogenetics, which combines fiber optics and genetic engineering to manipulate animal brains with once unimaginable speed and precision, the researchers activated these listless cells in the rats. "Their interest in cocaine basically vanished," Bonci says. The researchers suggested that stimulating the region of the human brain responsible for inhibiting behavior, in the prefrontal cortex, might quell an addict's insatiable urge to get high.

Gallimberti thought TMS might offer a practical way to do that. Our brains run on electrical impulses that zip among neurons with every thought and movement. Brain stimulation, which has been used for years to treat depression and migraines, taps that circuitry. The device is nothing but a coiled wire inside a wand. When electric current runs through it, the wand creates a magnetic pulse that alters electrical activity in the brain. Gallimberti thought repeated pulses might activate drug-damaged neural pathways, like a reboot on a frozen computer.

He and his partner, neurocognitive psychologist Alberto Terraneo, teamed up with Bonci to test the technique. They recruited a group of cocaine addicts: Sixteen underwent one month of brain stimulation while 13 received standard care, including medication for anxiety and depression. By the end of the trial, 11 people in the stimulation group, but only three in the other group, were drug free.

The investigators published their findings in the January 2016 issue of the journal *European Neuropsychopharmacology*. That prompted a flurry of publicity, which drew hundreds of cocaine users to the clinic. Perotti came in edgy and agitated. After his first session, he says, he felt calm. Soon he lost the desire for cocaine. It was still gone six months later. "It has been a complete change," he says. "I feel a vitality and desire to live that I had not felt for a long time."

It will take large, placebo-controlled trials to prove that the treatment works and the benefits last. The team plans to conduct further studies, and researchers around the world are testing brain stimulation to help people stop smoking, drinking, gambling, binge eating, and misusing opioids. "It's so promising," Bonci says. "Patients tell me, 'Cocaine used to be part of who I am. Now it's a distant thing that no longer controls me.'"

NOT LONG AGO THE IDEA of repairing the brain's wiring to fight addiction would have seemed far-fetched. But advances in neuroscience have upended conventional notions about addiction—what it is, what can trigger it, and why quitting is so tough. If you'd opened a medical textbook 30 years ago, you would have read that addiction means dependence on a substance with increasing tolerance, requiring more and more to feel the effects and producing a nasty withdrawal when use stops. That explained alcohol, nicotine, and heroin reasonably well. But it did not account for marijuana and cocaine, which typically don't cause the shakes, nausea, and vomiting of heroin withdrawal.

The old model also didn't explain perhaps the most insidious aspect of addiction: relapse. Why do people long for the burn of whiskey in the throat or the warm bliss of heroin after the body is no longer physically dependent?

The surgeon general's report reaffirms what the scientific establishment has been saying for years: Addiction is a disease, not a moral failing. It's characterized not necessarily by physical dependence or withdrawal but by compulsive repetition of an activity despite life-damaging consequences. This view has led many scientists to accept the once heretical idea that addiction is possible without drugs.

The most recent revision of the *Diagnostic and Statistical Manual of Mental Disorders,* the handbook of American psychiatry, for the first time recognizes a behavioral addiction: gambling. Some scientists believe that many allures of modern life—junk food, shopping, smartphones—are potentially addictive because of their powerful effects on the brain's reward system, the circuitry underlying craving.

"We are all exquisite reward detectors," says Anna Rose Childress, a clinical neuroscientist at the University of Pennsylvania's Center for Studies of Addiction. "It's our evolutionary legacy."

For years Childress and other scientists have tried to unravel the mysteries of addiction by studying the reward system. Much of Childress's research involves sliding people addicted to drugs into the tube of a magnetic resonance imaging (MRI) machine, which tracks blood flow in the brain as a way to analyze neural activity. Through complex algorithms and color-coding, brain scans are converted into images that pinpoint the circuits that kick into high gear when the brain lusts.

Childress, who has flaming red hair and a big laugh, sits at her computer, scrolling through a picture gallery of brains—gray ovals with bursts of color as vivid as a Disney movie. "It sounds nerdy, but I could look at these images for hours, and I do," she says. "They are little gifts. To think you can actually visualize a brain state that's so powerful and at the same time so dangerous. It's like reading tea leaves. All we see is spots that the computer turns into fuchsia and purple and green. But what are they trying to tell us?"

The reward system, a primitive part of the brain that isn't much different in rats, exists to ensure we seek what we need, and it alerts us to the sights, sounds, and scents that point us there. It operates in the realm of instinct and reflex, built for when survival depended on the ability to obtain food and sex before the competition got to them. But the system can trip us up in a world with 24/7 opportunities to fulfill our desires.

Desire depends on a complex cascade of brain actions, but scientists believe that the trigger for this is likely to be a spike in the neurotransmitter dopamine. A chemical messenger that carries signals across synapses, dopamine plays wide-ranging roles in the brain. Most relevant to addiction, the flow of dopamine heightens what scientists call salience, or the motivational

# 1.1 BILLION PEOPLE WORLDWIDE SMOKE TOBACCO

## CREATURE OF COMPULSION

This rat, in a simulation of a slot machine, is lured by the same types of flashing lights and throbbing sounds that keep humans playing in casinos. With a choice of openings that pay off in sugar pellets, the rat will consistently poke at the one with the biggest payoff but the smallest chance of winning. Using similar studies, Catharine Winstanley, a neuroscientist at the University of British Columbia, has discovered that a medication that blocks a dopamine receptor can reduce risky decision-making linked to compulsive gambling.

## IN THE GRIP OF GAMING

In Seoul, e-stadiums and gaming parlors charge about a dollar an hour, and some venues are open around the clock. Soon after South Korea made super-high-speed Internet cheap and widely available, it became clear that some people were ruining their lives through obsessive game playing. The government now pays for treatment. The American Psychiatric Association hasn't recognized compulsive gaming as an addiction, but it lists Internet gaming disorder as requiring more study.

# HIJACKING THE BRAIN

New research suggests that the brain's reward system has different mechanisms for craving and pleasure. Craving is driven by the neurotransmitter dopamine. Pleasure is stimulated by other neurotransmitters in "hedonic hot spots." When the craving circuitry overwhelms the pleasure hot spots, addiction occurs, leading people to pursue a behavior or drug despite the consequences.

## PATHWAYS TO CRAVING

Desire is triggered when dopamine, which originates near the top of the brain stem, travels through neural pathways to act on the brain. Drugs increase the flow of dopamine.

**Ventral tegmental area (VTA)**
Dopamine is produced here and flows outward along neurons distributed throughout the brain's reward system.

DOPAMINE

**Dorsal striatum**
Neurons here help form habits by identifying enjoyable patterns, such as the anticipation of buying drugs.

**Prefrontal cortex**
The amino acid glutamate, produced here, interacts with dopamine to spark visualizations that cue cravings.

**Amygdala**
Neurons here are stimulated by learned emotional responses, such as memories of cravings and pleasure.

**Brain stem**
Basic visceral sensations and reactions to pleasure, such as smiling, originate from this hot spot.

**Orbitofrontal cortex**
This hot spot gives a sense of gratification but is also the first to shut down if a person has indulged too much.

**Ventral pallidum**
Animal experiments show that damaging this hot spot can turn something that once gave pleasure into a source of disgust.

**Nucleus accumbens**
A hot spot within this key part of the craving circuitry amplifies the response to pleasure.

## PLEASURE HOT SPOTS

A system of small hedonic hot spots, unrelated to dopamine, provides temporary sensations of pleasure and forms a feedback loop with the reward system that controls desire.

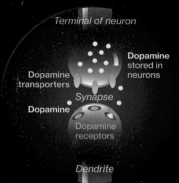

Terminal of neuron

Dopamine
transporters

**Dopamine**
stored in
neurons

**Dopamine**

Synapse

Dopamine
receptors

Dendrite

## NEURON ACTIVITY

**In a normal state**
Neurotransmitters carry
nerve impulses across
synapses between cells
to excite or inhibit activity.

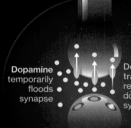

**Dopamine**
temporarily
floods
synapse

Dopamine
transporters
remove excess
dopamine from
synapse

**In an excited state**
Dopamine temporarily floods a
synapse when a pleasurable activity,
such as gambling, sex, shopping, or
gaming, is anticipated or experienced.

## A NATURAL HIGH

Our brains evolved a dopamine-based
reward system to encourage behaviors
that help us survive, such as eating,
procreating, and interacting socially.

Heroin
blocks
dopamine
inhibitors

Dopamine
inhibitor
receptors

*In VTA*

*In brain
reward
system*

**Dopamine**
floods
synapse

**On heroin**
Synapses flood with
dopamine when heroin
blocks dopamine
inhibitors in the VTA.

## A CHEMICAL RUSH

Different drugs interact with the reward
system in unique ways to keep synapses
artificially flooded with dopamine. That
dopamine rush can rewire your brain to
want more drugs, leading to addiction.

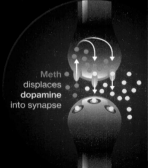

Meth
displaces
**dopamine**
into synapse

**On methamphetamine**
The drug reverses the natural,
controlled flow of dopamine
into neurons, forcing dopamine
to rush into synapses instead.

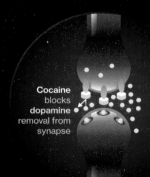

**Cocaine**
blocks
**dopamine**
removal from
synapse

**On cocaine**
By interfering with dopa-
mine transport, cocaine
prevents removal of excess
dopamine from synapses.

JASON TREAT AND RYAN T. WILLIAMS, NGM STAFF
ART: DANIEL HERTZBERG
SOURCE: KENT BERRIDGE, UNIVERSITY OF MICHIGAN

pull of a stimulus—cocaine, for instance, or reminders of it, such as a glimpse of white powder. Each drug that's abused affects brain chemistry in a distinct way, but they all send dopamine levels soaring far beyond the natural range. Wolfram Schultz, a University of Cambridge neuroscientist, calls the cells that make dopamine "the little devils in our brain," so powerfully does the chemical drive desire.

How powerfully? Consider the strange side effect of medications that mimic natural dopamine and are used to treat Parkinson's. The disease destroys dopamine-producing cells, primarily affecting movement. Dopamine-replacement drugs relieve the symptoms, but about 14 percent of Parkinson's patients who take these medications develop addictions to gambling, shopping, pornography, eating, or the medication itself. A report in the journal *Movement Disorders* describes three patients who became consumed by "reckless generosity," hooked on giving cash to strangers and friends they thought needed it.

Through learning, the signals or reminder cues for rewards come to provoke surges of dopamine. That's why the aroma of snickerdoodles baking in the oven, the ping of a text alert, or chatter spilling out the open door of a bar can yank a person's attention and trigger craving. Childress has shown that people who are addicted don't have to consciously register a cue for it to arouse their reward system. In a study published in *PLoS One* she scanned the brains of 22 recovering cocaine addicts while photos of crack pipes and other drug paraphernalia flashed before their eyes for 33 milliseconds, one-tenth the time it takes to blink. The men didn't consciously "see" anything, but the images activated the same parts of the reward circuitry that visible drug cues excite.

In Childress's view the findings support stories she has heard from cocaine patients who relapsed yet couldn't explain what prompted it. "They were walking around in environments where most of the time one thing or another had been signals for cocaine," she says. "They were basically getting primed, having that ancient reward system tingled. By the time they became conscious of it, it was like a snowball rolling downhill."

THE BRAIN, OF COURSE, is more than an organ of reward. It houses evolution's most sophisticated machinery for thinking, considering risks, and controlling runaway desire. Why do craving and habits overpower reason, good intentions, and awareness of the toll of addiction?

"There's a strong-ass demon that messes you up," says a burly man with a booming voice who smokes crack regularly.

He sits in a black swivel chair in a small windowless room at the Icahn School of Medicine at Mount Sinai in Manhattan, waiting for his MRI. He's taking part in a study in the lab of Rita Z. Goldstein, a professor of psychiatry and neuroscience, about the role of the brain's executive control center, the prefrontal cortex. While the scanner records his brain activity, he'll view pictures of cocaine with instructions to imagine either the pleasures or the perils that each image evokes. Goldstein and her team are testing whether neurofeedback, which allows people to observe their brains in action, can help addicts take more control over compulsive habits.

"I keep thinking, I can't believe I've wasted all that damn money on the drug," the man says as he's led to the MRI machine. "It never balances out, what you gain versus what you lose."

Goldstein's neuroimaging studies helped expand understanding of the brain's reward system by exploring how addiction is associated with the prefrontal cortex and other cortical regions. Changes in this part of the brain affect judgment, self-control, and other cognitive functions tied to addiction. "Reward is important in the beginning of the addiction cycle, but the response to reward is reduced as the disorder continues," she says. People with addiction often persist in using drugs to relieve the misery they feel when they stop.

In 2002, working with Nora Volkow, now the director of NIDA, Goldstein published what has become an influential model of addiction, called iRISA, or impaired response inhibition and salience attribution. That's a mouthful of a name for a fairly simple idea. As drug cues gain prominence, the field of attention narrows, like a camera zooming in on one object and pushing everything else out of view. Meanwhile the brain's ability to control behavior in the face of those cues diminishes.

Goldstein has shown that as a group, cocaine addicts have reduced gray matter volume in the prefrontal cortex, a structural deficiency associated with poorer executive function, and they perform differently from people who aren't addicted on psychological tests of memory, attention, decision-making, and the processing of nondrug rewards such as money. They generally perform worse, but not always. It depends on the context.

For example, on a standard task that measures fluency—how many farm animals can you name in a minute?—people with addiction may lag. But when Goldstein asks them to list words related to drugs, they tend to outperform everyone else. Chronic drug users are often great at planning and executing tasks that involve using drugs, but this bias may compromise other cognitive processes, including knowing how and when to stop. The behavioral and brain impairments are sometimes more subtle than in other brain disorders, and they're more heavily influenced by the situation.

"We think that is one of the reasons why addiction has been and still is one of the last disorders to be recognized as a disorder of the brain," she says.

Goldstein's studies don't answer the chicken-and-egg question: Does addiction cause these impairments, or do brain vulnerabilities due to genetics, trauma, stress, or other factors increase the risk of becoming addicted? But Goldstein's lab has discovered tantalizing evidence that frontal brain regions begin to heal when people stop using drugs. A 2016 study tracked 19 cocaine addicts who had abstained or severely cut back for six months. They showed significant increases in gray matter volume in two regions involved in inhibiting behavior and evaluating rewards.

MARC POTENZA STRIDES through the cavernous Venetian casino in Las Vegas. Electronic games—slot machines, roulette, blackjack, poker—beep and clang and trill. Potenza, an affable and energetic psychiatrist at Yale University and director of the school's Program for Research on Impulsivity and Impulse Control Disorders, hardly seems to notice. "I'm not a gambler," he says with a slight shrug and a grin. Out of the pleasure palazzo, he heads down an escalator and through a long concourse to a sedate meeting room in the Sands Expo Convention Center, where he will present his research on gambling addiction to about a hundred scientists and clinicians.

The meeting is organized by the National Center for Responsible Gaming, an industry-supported group that has funded gambling research by Potenza and others. It takes place on the eve of the industry's mega convention, the Global Gaming Expo. Potenza stands at the podium, talking about white matter integrity and cortical blood flow in gamblers. Just beyond the room, expo exhibitors are setting up displays touting innovations engineered to get dopamine flowing in millennials. E-sports betting. Casino games modeled on Xbox. More than 27,000 game manufacturers, designers, and casino operators will attend.

Potenza and other scientists pushed the psychiatric establishment to accept the idea of behavioral addiction. In 2013 the American Psychiatric Association moved problem gambling out of a chapter called "Impulse Control Not Elsewhere Classified" in the *Diagnostic and Statistical Manual* and into the chapter called "Substance-Related and Addictive Disorders." This was no mere technicality. "It breaks the dam for considering other behaviors as addiction," says Judson Brewer, director of research at the Center for Mindfulness at the University of Massachusetts Medical School.

The association considered the matter for more than a decade while research accumulated on how gambling resembles drug addiction.

# 91
## AMERICANS DIE EACH DAY FROM OPIOID OVERDOSES

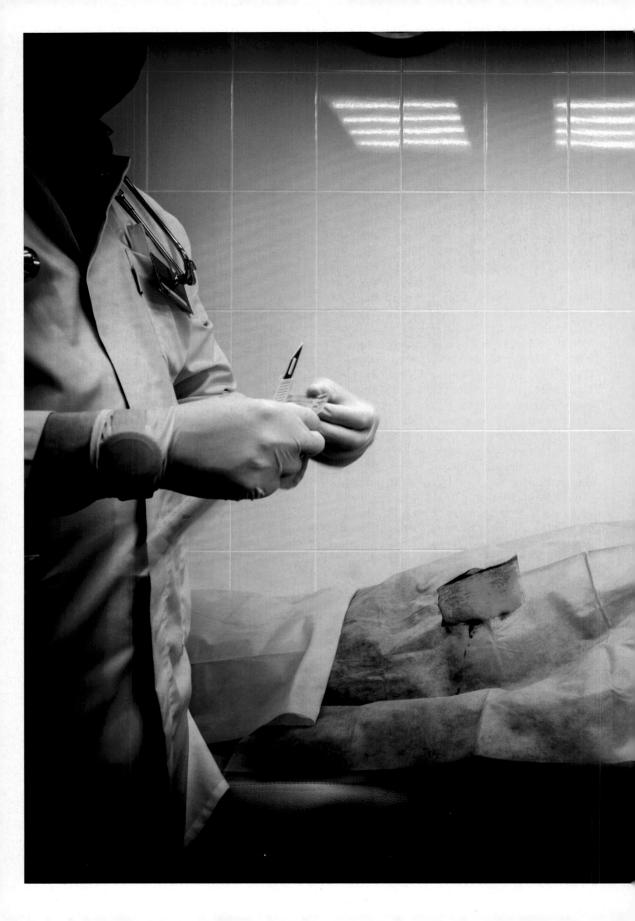

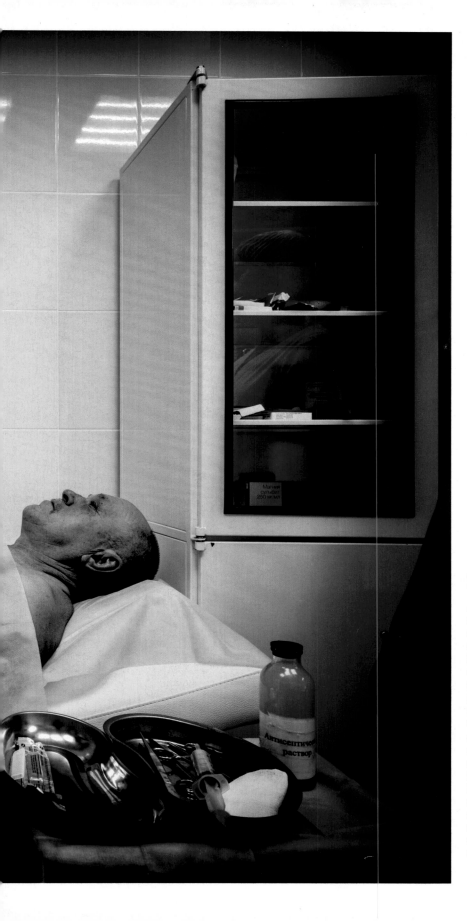

## AVERSION TACTICS

At Marshak Clinic, a drug-treatment center near Moscow, a six-month dose of Antabuse is implanted under the skin of a recovering alcoholic about to be discharged after a 30-day stay. The medication will cause him to vomit if he drinks, a form of aversion therapy. The clinic also relies heavily on other strategies to try to break the addiction, including yoga, individual and group counseling sessions, amino acid supplements, dietary changes, and antidepressants.

## CASUAL DRINKING

Sylvie Imbert and Yves Brasey credit baclofen, a medication used to treat muscle spasms, with freeing them from their devotion to the bottle. In studies, baclofen has shown promise for treating alcohol dependency. Brasey, having a beer at the Hotel Luxembourg Parc in Paris, now has just a few drinks at a time. Imbert had six to nine drinks almost daily until she started taking baclofen. Now she drinks only occasionally. Imbert and Brasey have become outspoken advocates for the drug.

Insatiable desire, preoccupation, and uncontrollable urges. The fast thrill and the need to keep upping the ante to feel the fireworks. An inability to stop, despite promises and resolve. Potenza did some of the first brain-imaging studies of gamblers and discovered that they looked similar to scans of drug addicts, with sluggish activity in the parts of the brain responsible for impulse control.

NOW THAT THE PSYCHIATRIC establishment accepts the idea that addiction is possible without drugs, researchers are trying to determine what types of behaviors qualify as addictions. Are all pleasurable activities potentially addictive? Or are we medicalizing every habit, from the minute-to-minute glance at email to the late-afternoon candy break?

In the United States the *Diagnostic and Statistical Manual* now lists Internet gaming disorder as a condition worthy of more study, along with chronic, debilitating grief and caffeine-use disorder. Internet addiction didn't make it.

But it makes psychiatrist Jon Grant's list of addictions. So do compulsive shopping and sex, food addiction, and kleptomania. "Anything that's overly rewarding, anything that induces euphoria or is calming, can be addictive," says Grant, who runs the Addictive, Compulsive and Impulsive Disorders Clinic at the University of Chicago. Whether it will be addictive depends on a person's vulnerability, which is affected by genetics, trauma, and depression, among other factors. "We don't all get addicted," he says.

Perhaps the most controversial of the "new" addictions are food and sex. Can a primal desire be addictive? The World Health Organization has recommended including compulsive sex as an impulse control disorder in its next edition of the *International Classification of Diseases,* due out by 2018. But the American Psychiatric Association rejected compulsive sex for its latest diagnostic manual, after serious debate about whether the problem is real. The association didn't consider food addiction.

Nicole Avena, a neuroscientist at Mount Sinai St. Luke's Hospital in New York, has shown that rats will keep gobbling sugar if you let them, and they develop tolerance, craving, and withdrawal, just as they do when they get hooked on cocaine. She says high-fat foods and highly processed foods such as refined flour may be as problematic as sugar. Avena and researchers at the University of Michigan recently surveyed 384 adults: Ninety-two percent reported a persistent desire to eat certain foods and repeated unsuccessful attempts to stop, two hallmarks of addiction. The respondents ranked pizza—typically made with a white-flour crust and topped with sugar-laden tomato sauce—as the most addictive food, with chips and chocolate tied for second place. Avena has no doubt food addiction is real. "That's a major reason why people struggle with obesity."

SCIENCE HAS BEEN MORE SUCCESSFUL in charting what goes awry in the addicted brain than in devising ways to fix it. A few medications can help people overcome certain addictions. For example, naltrexone was developed to treat opioid misuse, but it's also prescribed to help cut down or stop drinking, binge eating, and gambling.

Buprenorphine activates opioid receptors in the brain but to a much lesser degree than heroin does. The medication suppresses the awful symptoms of craving and withdrawal so people can break addictive patterns. "It's a miracle," says Justin Nathanson, a filmmaker and gallery owner in Charleston, South Carolina. He used heroin for years and tried rehab twice but relapsed. Then a doctor prescribed buprenorphine. "In five minutes I felt completely normal," he says. He hasn't used heroin for 13 years.

Most medications used to treat addiction have been around for years. The latest advances in neuroscience have yet to produce a breakthrough cure. Researchers have tested dozens of compounds, but while many show promise in the lab, results in clinical trials have been mixed at best. Brain stimulation for addiction treatment, an outgrowth of recent neuroscience discoveries, is still experimental.

Although 12-step programs, cognitive therapy, and other psychotherapeutic approaches are transformative for many people, they don't work for everyone, and relapse rates are high.

In the world of addiction treatment, there are two camps. One believes that a cure lies in fixing the faulty chemistry or wiring of the addicted brain through medication or techniques like TMS, with psychosocial support as an adjunct. The other sees medication as the adjunct, a way to reduce craving and the agony of withdrawal while allowing people to do the psychological work essential to addiction recovery. Both camps agree on one thing: Current treatment falls short. "Meanwhile my patients are suffering," says Brewer, the mindfulness researcher in Massachusetts.

Brewer is a student of Buddhist psychology. He's also a psychiatrist who specializes in addiction. He believes the best hope for treating addiction lies in melding modern science and ancient contemplative practice. He's an evangelist for mindfulness, which uses meditation and other techniques to bring awareness to what we're doing and feeling, especially to habits that drive self-defeating behavior.

In Buddhist philosophy, craving is viewed as the root of all suffering. The Buddha wasn't talking about heroin or ice cream or some of the other compulsions that bring people to Brewer's groups. But there's growing evidence that mindfulness can counter the dopamine flood of contemporary life. Researchers at the University of Washington showed that a program based on mindfulness was more effective in preventing drug-addiction relapse than 12-step programs. In a head-to-head comparison, Brewer showed that mindfulness training was twice as effective as the gold-standard behavioral antismoking program.

Mindfulness trains people to pay attention to cravings without reacting to them. The idea is to ride out the wave of intense desire. Mindfulness also encourages people to notice why they feel pulled to indulge. Brewer and others have shown that meditation quiets the posterior cingulate cortex, the neural space involved in the kind of rumination that can lead to a loop of obsession.

Brewer speaks in the soothing tones you'd want in your therapist. His sentences toggle between scientific terms—hippocampus, insula—and Pali, a language of Buddhist texts. On a recent evening he stands in front of 23 stress eaters, who sit in a semicircle in beige molded plastic chairs, red round cushions nestling their stockinged feet.

Donnamarie Larievy, a marketing consultant and executive coach, joined the weekly mindfulness group to break her ice cream and chocolate habit. Four months in, she eats healthier food and enjoys an occasional scoop of double fudge but rarely yearns for it. "It has been a life changer," she says. "Bottom line, my cravings have decreased."

NATHAN ABELS HAS DECIDED to stop drinking—several times. In July 2016 he ended up in the emergency room at the Medical University of South Carolina in Charleston, hallucinating after a three-day, gin-fueled bender. While undergoing treatment, he volunteered for a TMS study by neuroscientist Colleen A. Hanlon.

For Abels, 28, a craftsman and lighting design technician who understands how circuitry works, the insights of neuroscience provide a sense of relief. He doesn't feel trapped by biology or stripped of responsibility for his drinking. Instead he feels less shame. "I forever thought of drinking as a weakness," he says. "There's so much power in understanding it's a disease."

He's throwing everything that the medical center offers at his recovery—medication, psychotherapy, support groups, and electromagnetic zaps to the head. "The brain can rebuild itself," he says. "That's the most amazing thing." □

# 3.3
## MILLION WORLDWIDE DIE EACH YEAR FROM ALCOHOL

**Fran Smith** is a writer and editor. This is her first article for *National Geographic*. **Max Aguilera-Hellweg** is a photographer who also trained as a medical doctor. His last assignment for the magazine was "Beyond Reasonable Doubt," in the July 2016 issue.

## PATIENTS,
## NOT PRISONERS

The law enforcement officers arresting this man on suspicion of smoking heroin in downtown Seattle chose to refer him to a treatment program for certain low-level drug offenders, rather than take him to jail. The innovative program, under way for more than five years, reflects an increasing awareness that habitual drug abuse stems from addiction and can be treated as a disease, not a crime. The program has reduced recidivism among offenders diverted from the criminal justice system.

# HOOKED
## AT BIRTH

B abies going through opioid withdrawal have a distinct way of crying: a short, anguished, high-pitched wail repeated over and over. It echoes through the neonatal therapeutic unit of Cabell Huntington Hospital in Huntington, West Virginia. A week-old girl has been at it, inconsolably, since six o'clock in the morning. At ten o'clock Sara Murray, the unit's soft-spoken, no-nonsense nurse manager, sighs. "This may be a frustrating day," she says.

The nation's escalating opioid crisis is painfully evident in this hospital, where one in five newborns has been exposed to heroin or other drugs in the womb. "What you're seeing here is the tip of the iceberg of substance use," says neonatologist Sean Loudin, the unit's medical director.

West Virginia leads the nation in the rate of fatal opioid overdoses. Cabell County, which averaged about 130 overdose calls to 911 annually until 2012, had 1,476 calls last year, many of which saved lives. The youngest victim, who lived, was 11.

In 2012, after the neonatal intensive care unit became so overwhelmed by drug-dependent babies it had to turn away newborns with other medical needs, the hospital opened this unit. It typically has 18 babies. On this day there are 23.

They struggle to overcome the powerful effects of addictive drugs on the brain. The babies shake, sweat, vomit, and hold their bodies stiff as planks. They eat and sleep fitfully. Swaddled, they lie in clear plastic bassinets or in the arms of nurses, parents, or volunteer cuddlers. These babies need calm and quiet. Many also need methadone to relieve their symptoms, and they are weaned from it over days or weeks.

The big problem used to be exposure to painkillers. Then heroin. Now it's heroin plus cocaine, methamphetamine, and lately, an anticonvulsant called gabapentin.

Many babies are sicker, and they need care longer.

"OK," Murray says gently, lifting a bleating 41-day-old boy to her chest. She places a green pacifier in his mouth. While he sucks like a piston, fast and hard, she cradles him firmly and sways almost imperceptibly. Soon his jaw relaxes, his eyelids flutter, and he drifts off to sleep. —FS

### HOW TO GET HELP

For more information about drug addiction and treatments, go to *drugabuse.gov*.

## COMFORTING NEWBORNS

This five-week-old boy is one of nearly 300 infants a year treated for opioid withdrawal at Cabell Huntington Hospital in West Virginia. He sleeps under the soothing touch of his mother, Jordann Thomas, 28, who's in recovery from heroin addiction. Doctors treated the baby with methadone, then weaned him from it. He's gaining weight, sleeping well, and ready to go home. "Without this program, I don't know where I'd be," Thomas says.

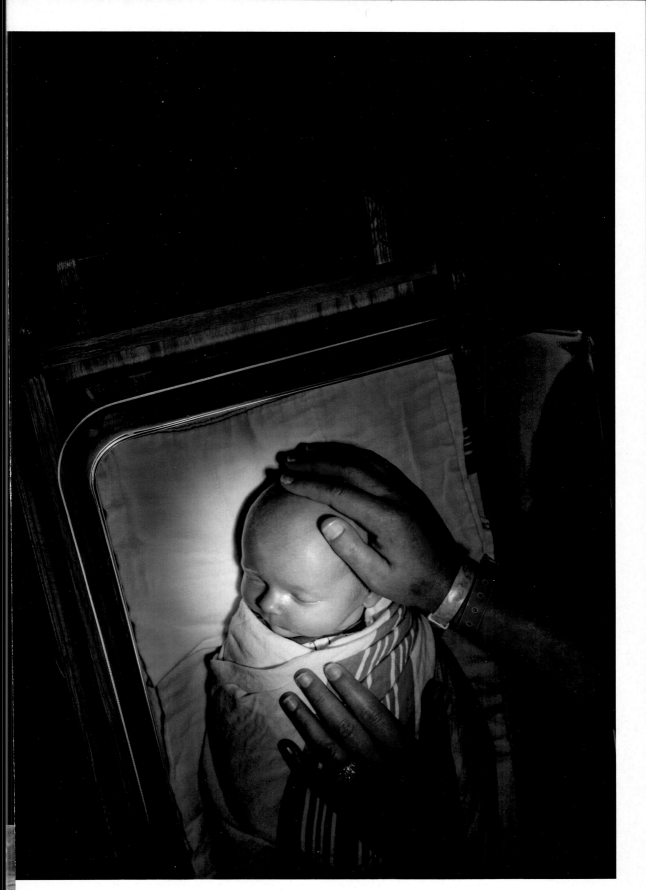

# Stewards of the Sea

*As fish populations crash elsewhere, communities in Mexico's Baja California are limiting catches to keep harvests*

A free diver swims with bigeye trevallies in the Gulf of California near Cabo Pulmo. Since the gulf's only true coral reef became a no-take zone, biomass has increased by two to three times.

WATCH  Thomas P. Peschak swims through a "fish tornado" in Cabo Pulmo and coaxes a whale to swim closer to a boat in Laguna San Ignacio. To see the videos, go to *ngm.com/Sep2017.*

**A great white shark** swims in the Isla Guadalupe Biosphere Reserve, 160 miles off Baja California. As one of two places in the world where these sharks congregate in clear water, it's a magnet for adventurous dive tourists. Ecotourism in Baja brings hundreds of millions of dollars to Mexico.

By Erik Vance
Photographs by Thomas P. Peschak

# It's a half hour before sunrise, and the ocean appears inky black as it slaps against the sand.

A dozen fishermen are lounging in the boat master's office in Punta Abreojos, laughing and talking about the party they'll have that night.

The mood is festive in this hamlet at the midpoint of Mexico's Baja California peninsula because today is a day the town looks forward to all year long—the opening of abalone season. Actually the season opened four months earlier, but Punta Abreojos observes an unusual self-imposed ban. Rather than fish for abalone as soon as the government allows, in January, the community waits until April, when the shellfish have put on more weight.

I head out into the Pacific Ocean with three fishermen in their 50s who have been working together since they were teenagers. "Horse" runs the engine, "Mole" hauls up the bags of abalones, and "Fish," naturally, is the diver. (They are Porfirio Zúñiga, Eduardo Liera, and Luis Arce, but no one here calls them that.)

Fish is in especially high spirits—he's just returned from Pebble Beach, California, where he surfed and played golf. His buddies poke fun at him as he slips into a crisp new wet suit. The sun is up, and the water has turned from black to deep blue. Before they arrive at their fishing spot, Horse stops the boat over a reef crawling with abalones. "Those are the green abalone," Mole says. "They won't be ready for a month at least."

A few miles later Fish hops into the water. Within two hours he's hit the catch limit and comes up with a smile and a bag full of healthy abalones. In most fishing towns in Mexico—or

Octavio Aburto dives near Isla Espíritu Santo, in the Gulf of California. The marine biologist studies why some reserves succeed and others fail. He's found the secret is in the community that lives there. "You start creating pride," he says, "a commitment to recovery."

in much of the rest of the developing world, for that matter—men like these would be pulling a meager catch out of depleted waters, living hand to mouth. What makes these men so optimistic about the season ahead? How can they afford new gear and vacations at elite golf courses?

The town's fishing cooperative started in 1948 and for years operated like others—taking as much from the sea as it could. But in the 1970s, after a few disappointing harvests, the fishermen decided to try something new. They would manage the lobster (and later the abalone) for the long term instead of immediate profits.

Today Abreojos and a few like-minded Baja communities following the same strategy catch more than 90 percent of Mexico's abalones. Houses in Abreojos are freshly painted. The town has a baseball team and a surfing team. The lobster and abalone are canned at a modern processing plant and sold directly to Asia, maximizing profits. The

PHOTOGRAPHIC COVERAGE FOR THIS STORY WAS SUPPORTED BY THE SAVE OUR SEAS FOUNDATION.

town's waters are guarded using radar, boats, and planes. Retired fishermen collect pensions.

Perhaps no one better reflects this success than 67-year-old Zacarías Zúñiga. His father helped found the cooperative yet struggled to make his daily catch. Zúñiga works as a quality control specialist in the cannery. Thanks to a scholarship to college offered by the cooperative, his son is a computer science professor.

"We all work, and at the same time we all are owners," he says.

Punta Abreojos is not the only success story in this part of Mexico. Around the world, fish populations are crashing, and species such as tuna, turtle, and grouper are ever more scarce. Yet, in northwestern Mexico, a few communities have managed to protect their underwater resources. These micro-conservation areas were created by or with the support of the communities, which many environmentalists see as the key to

conservation that works. How they did it holds lessons for the world's fishing communities.

THE HISTORY OF BAJA FISHING is a saga of booms and busts. When author John Steinbeck visited the peninsula in 1940, he marveled at the incredible biodiversity—huge schools of manta rays, beds of pearl oysters, and so many turtles that older people here say you could cross the sea walking on their shells. But within a couple decades, man had found the limits, decimating the wild oyster beds. After that he turned to turtles, tuna, sharks, groupers, and a dozen other species.

The Mexican government, making things worse, for decades encouraged unemployed workers to become fishermen in a program called March to the Sea. In southern Baja, which didn't become a Mexican state until 1974, this led to a lone-cowboy culture that persists.

"People are used to doing things on their own,"

A school of pygmy devil rays gobbles up plankton near Isla Espíritu Santo, once a gathering place for sharks and rays. They declined dramatically in the 1990s as global demand for seafood soared. Since then, thanks to local conservation efforts, many populations have made recoveries.

# There's a time for journalistic detachment. But when a young whale leans up against your boat, seemingly wanting to be petted, that is not such a time.

says Octavio Aburto, a marine biologist with Scripps Institution of Oceanography who has studied Baja fisheries for 20 years. "They are not expecting the government to do things." A native of Mexico City, Aburto first came to the region in the 1990s and fell in love with its congenial fishing culture and beguiling underwater safari.

After decades of overfishing, though, the region was seeing fishery collapse of target species as families moved from camp to camp chasing the remaining fish. In a few places small communities began to devise ways to maintain their resources. Eventually their ideas spread.

From these scattered success stories, five rules emerge as the key to sustainable, community-supported ocean management. First, like Abreojos, it helps if the site is fairly isolated, with just a community or two using it. Second, the community needs a resource of high value, such as lobster or abalone. Strong, visionary community leaders are the third necessity. Fourth, fishermen need a way to support themselves while the resources recover. And, lastly, the community must be bound together by trust.

In Baja several communities besides Abreojos illustrate the importance of these rules. One remarkable example of a high-value resource can be seen—and touched—in Laguna San Ignacio, a few miles down the coast.

In 1972, according to local legend, Francisco "Pachico" Mayoral was fishing in his usual spot in the lagoon. As fishermen did in that region, he carried an oar to bang against the boat whenever a gray whale swam too close. Gray whales, everyone thought, were dangerous creatures capable of snapping a boat in half. Before long,

one sidled up to his boat. Perhaps it was curiosity or daring, but for some reason Mayoral reached out to touch it. The whale leaned in and allowed him to stroke its smooth, spongy skin. And in that moment a cottage industry was born. By the late 1980s Mayoral and other fishermen were guiding tourists to the whales by the dozens.

Today whale-watching is among the most important economic activities in the region, with ecotourism lodges now dotting the shoreline. Incredibly the gray whales and their calves still cuddle up to boats, though no one is sure why.

Just as incredible is how the people there have managed it. Unlike Bahía Magdalena to the south, where guides chase down the animals in free-for-all whale-petting hunts, San Ignacio limits the number of boats on the water to around 16. Fishing in the lagoon is banned during the whale-watching season, so the whales have some peace and quiet with their young offspring.

The preservation of this natural estuary does more than protect the whales; it also protects crucial nursery habitats for fish and invertebrates. In the mid-1990s Mitsubishi tried to build a saltworks near the mouth of the lagoon that could have had a deleterious effect on the ecosystem. The community, with the help of environmental organizations, mobilized a fierce campaign to block the project and eventually succeeded.

I head into the bay on a 24-foot *panga* with tourists hoping to have the absurdly unique experience of petting a whale. Roberto Fischer, the fisherman taking us on the water, warns that there's no guarantee we will touch or even see a whale. They must choose to come to us; we aren't allowed to chase them. A few hundred yards off, a warden paid by the community eyes us to make sure we follow the rules. Suddenly a whale spout appears and a jolt of excitement rocks the boat.

"I see it! Did you see it?" shouts a tourist. Timidly a mother gray whale comes over to inspect us. Her calf approaches less timidly, and soon it's popping up on either side of the boat as the tourists cautiously stick out their hands. The mother joins in, and a third also takes a passing interest.

"It's whale soup!" Fischer says. There's a time for journalistic detachment. But when a young

# Protecting Baja Seas

Ocean conservationists often call the Gulf of California the "aquarium of the world," but overfishing has threatened the remarkable diversity and quantity of its sea life. Now local communities, in partnership with nonprofits and the Mexican government, are working to protect what is left.

## Protected Areas

- Isla Guadalupe Biosphere Reserve
- El Vizcaíno Biosphere Reserve
- Archipiélago de Revillagigedo Biosphere Reserve
- Islands and Protected Areas of the Gulf of California (World Heritage site)

→ Gray whale migration route

⌑ Gray whale nursery

◆ Sea turtle nesting area

**ISOLATED ISLE**
The pristine waters around this sparsely inhabited island are one of the best spots in the world to observe great white sharks.

ISLA GUADALUPE BIOSPHERE RESERVE

**WHALE HAVEN**
Every year gray whales and their calves migrate to the safety of the shallow, warm waters of three Baja lagoons, including still undeveloped San Ignacio within El Vizcaíno Biosphere Reserve.

**OCEAN CROSSROADS**
Four remote volcanic islands at the junction of two ocean currents create a biologically rich ecosystem. The protected area abounds with hungry manta rays, sharks, whales, and seabirds.

**UNIQUE SPECIES**
The islands of Baja California, long isolated, boast a high number of endemic species. More than 240 islands and coastal and marine protected areas in the gulf now make up a single World Heritage site.

MAP AREA

MEXICO

PACIFIC OCEAN

Tijuana
CALIFORNIA
Ensenada
Mexicali ★
UNITED STATES
Colorado

BAJA CALIFORNIA

UPPER GULF OF CALIFORNIA AND COLORADO RIVER DELTA BIOSPHERE RESERVE

San Felipe

Punta Baja

Southbound November–February

Bahía Sebastián Vizcaíno

Isla Cedros

Isla Natividad

Isla Ángel de la Guarda

EL VIZCAÍNO BIOSPHERE RESERVE

Great white shark nursery

Guerrero Negro

Isla Tiburón

ARCHIPIÉLAGO SAN LORENZO NATIONAL PARK

Laguna Ojo de Liebre

WHALE SANCTUARY OF EL VIZCAÍNO

ISLA SAN PEDRO MARTIR BIOSPHERE RESERVE

Sierra de San Francisco

Punta Abreojos

Laguna San Ignacio

Santa Rosalía

MEXICO

Guaymas

BAJA CALIF. SUR

Cabo San Lázaro

Loreto

I. Carmen

BAHÍA DE LORETO N.P.

Gulf of California (Sea of Cortez)

Ciudad Obregón

Bahía Magdalena

Northbound February–May

Isla Santa Margarita

I. San José

I. Espíritu Santo

La Paz ★

Bahía de La Paz

Los Mochis

I. Cerralvo

Protected island

Culiacán

CABO PULMO NATIONAL PARK

Cabo San Lucas

Isla Clarión

ARCHIPIÉLAGO DE REVILLAGIGEDO BIOSPHERE RESERVE

Isla Roca Partida

Isla San Benedicto

Isla Socorro

Mazatlán

ISLA ISABEL N.P.

↑N

0 mi 80
0 km 80

ISLAS MARÍAS BIOSPHERE RESERVE

ISLAS MARIETAS N.P.

Tuxpan

MATTHEW W. CHWASTYK, NGM STAFF
SOURCES: JUAN BEZAURY-CREEL, THE NATURE CONSERVANCY; JORGE URBÁN RAMÍREZ, LAGUNA SAN IGNACIO ECOSYSTEM SCIENCE PROGRAM; JEFFREY SEMINOFF, NOAA; ERIK VANCE; THE STATE OF THE WORLD'S SEA TURTLES

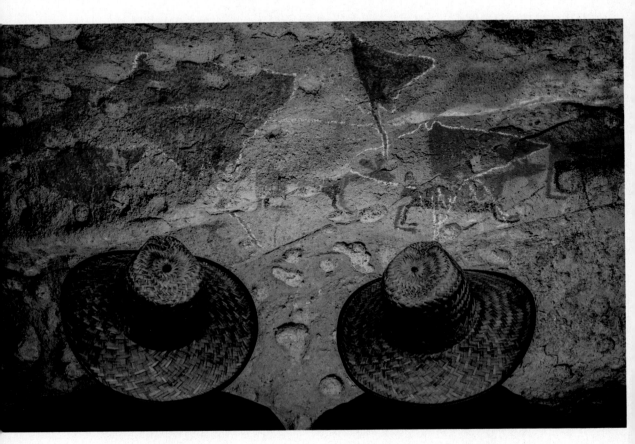

The waters off Baja were so rich in the 1940s that older people say you could cross the sea walking on turtles. But within a couple decades, man had found the limits.

PHOTO ABOVE TAKEN WITH PERMISSION FROM CONSEJO NACIONAL PARA LA CULTURA Y LAS ARTES (CONACULTA), INSTITUTO NACIONAL DE ANTROPOLOGÍA E HISTORIA (INAH), MEXICO

Ocean life figures prominently in Baja history. Pre-Hispanic cultures painted rays, sharks, dolphins, tuna, and seals in the remote canyons of the Sierra de San Francisco mountain range (left). Today these animals play an important role in tourism in places like Mexico's Archipiélago de Revillagigedo Biosphere Reserve, in the Pacific Ocean about 240 miles southwest of Baja's southern tip. Divers there see sights like a manta ray being cleaned by Clarion angelfish (above).

A northern elephant seal pup peers into the camera near Isla Guadalupe while other juveniles play nearby. Reserves create sanctuaries where once nearly extinct species can reproduce. How to maximize this ability to restock populations is a key question in ocean conservation today.

For conservation to work, community cohesion and trust are essential. In rural Baja, trust in one's neighbor can be hard to find, but it's possible to create it.

Baja communities employ different strategies to make a living from the ocean's resources. Some rely on tourism, including a former fisherman in Bahía Magdalena who takes visitors to see sharks, whales, and pelicans diving for fish (left). Magdalena has suffered from failed conservation efforts, whereas to the north the people of Punta Abreojos carefully manage their resources for high-value products like abalone and lobster (above).

# The Earth's five largest protected areas are marine parks. Ocean life rebounds within their borders. But what kinds of habitats yield the best ecological results?

whale leans up against your boat and opens its mouth, seemingly wanting to be petted, that is not such a time. I reach out my hand and touch the soft, knobby skin and then, astonishingly, pet its tongue. The massive creature looks at the dumbfounded writer and slides back into the water.

NOWHERE IS THE THIRD RULE of successful marine conservation—the need for visionary leaders—more evident than in Cabo Pulmo. In the 1980s it was a backwater fishing village near the tip of Baja. Too small and poor to afford ice machines to cool fish and to maintain roads to get them to market, Cabo Pulmo supported just a few fishermen, some of whom worked the reef—the only true coral one in the Gulf of California—just offshore. In the mid-1980s, locals say, biologists visited and loaned the fishermen a diving mask. What they saw alarmed them—pockmarks from their anchors and overturned coral heads everywhere. And very few fish.

"We saw the reef like it was our own garden. But not like an ecosystem," says Judith Castro, a community leader. "The fishermen didn't know about the damage they were doing."

In the early 1990s Castro's brother Mario, a fisherman and diver, and Tito Mijares, a bar owner, led Cabo Pulmo's fishermen to make a bold decision to support a marine reserve. By 1995 most fishing was forbidden in a 27-square-mile area, creating a legal no-take reserve—the only well-enforced one in the region. It's not big, but it turns out you don't need much space to bring back an ocean community. Today Cabo Pulmo National Park has two to three times more biomass than in 2000 and a vibrant economy now based on diving tourism.

If your community boasts the area's only coral reef or a pod of affection-hungry whales, developing a tourism model is an excellent way to save a threatened ecosystem. But not every fishing village has that luxury. Besides, tourism doesn't create many jobs. In San Ignacio it supports only about 200 people and only for a few months a year. Then they go back to fishing.

This brings up the fourth rule. For conservation to work, fishermen need a way to make money while they wait for their resource to recover. And the conservation efforts need manpower. To this end the community of El Manglito—on the estuary that borders the city of La Paz—has adopted an interesting strategy.

Fishermen once harvested shellfish with abandon from the broad, shallow bay west of town. By 2009 very few were left. With financial support from Noroeste Sustentable, a nonprofit in La Paz, the fishermen—many of whom had turned to poaching—stopped fishing and began managing their resources. They were paid to watch for poachers and to do biological surveys estimating the amount of shellfish, now mostly a scallop-like creature called *callo de hacha*. The first survey estimated that fewer than 100,000 shellfish were left. Today it's more like 2.3 million.

"It's always said that fishermen are the ones that destroy species, but not anymore. The sea has already given a lot. Now we give something back," says Antonio "Chiflo" Méndez, a fisherman.

El Manglito and Noroeste Sustentable did a lot right to bring the fishery back to life. But most important, the fishermen guarding or assessing the resource received salaries while the shellfish recovered. Paying them turned them from fishermen into professional environmental stewards.

THE LAST RULE is perhaps the hardest to follow. For conservation to work, community cohesion and trust are essential. In places such as Abreojos and El Manglito, locals enforce the fishing bans when it comes to outsiders, but there is also a fundamental presumption that people in the community will play by the rules.

In rural Baja, trust in one's neighbor can be hard to find, but it's possible to create it. At least that's what a conservation organization called Niparajá, based in La Paz, is betting on. Niparajá works on sustainable fisheries in an especially desolate region of southeastern Baja, along the Loreto–La Paz corridor. Along the ragged shorelines and breathtaking vistas there are few people and even fewer roads. But those isolated fishing communities overlook some of the best unprotected habitat in the region.

When Niparajá started working in those communities, it didn't focus on fishing. Instead it promoted soccer tournaments. "How do you start building trust?" asks Amy Hudson Weaver, who coordinates the program. "You don't start by talking about fishing. You've got to be like, Is this guy going to kick me in the shin, or is he going to respect the rules? Is he someone I can trust?"

Sponsoring soccer tournaments in tiny towns might seem like a waste of time and money, but it slowly built trust between villages that have jealously guarded fishing grounds from each other. Next Niparajá took some fishermen to Cabo Pulmo to see the impact a fishing ban can have on ocean life. Eventually, after years of discussions, the villages decided to try conservation. Each selected a small area and agreed not to fish in it for five years. The areas are not big—the largest is just under three square miles—but it was a start.

"The idea is to have like a savings account," says José Manuel Rondero, a 35-year-old fisherman who has watched lobster and fish populations plummet.

To monitor the reserves, Niparajá struck on a clever idea. Each year it charters a research vessel for a trip down a 60-mile stretch of the corridor with biology students, government scientists, and fishermen from each community.

Rondero rolls his eyes when told I'll be trailing him. We drop into the water near a steep underwater slope. Many of the fishermen on the boat have dived in the Cabo Pulmo reserve, but several tell me they were unimpressed. Sure, there are a lot of fish, but nothing compared with what the corridor could have.

I see what they mean. The countless nooks and boulders are perfect habitat. Rondero takes out a tape measure, pulls it out 30 meters, and

swims along it with a clipboard, counting fish one way and invertebrates the other. Then he sits and counts all the fish in his field of view.

The totals are a little dismal—a few lone fish and some urchins. Once we are out of the water, Rondero explains that this no-fishing zone is small and very new. In the bigger ones he's seen biodiversity increase in just a couple of years, from a few goatfish to huge groupers, grunts, and parrotfish. A few miles north of here, one marine reserve has blossomed recently, and the communities have decided to expand it. "This year is better than all of the past years I've seen," he says. "I'm seeing it very replenished. Lots of fish."

From a scientific perspective, this research is crucial. The five largest protected areas on Earth are marine parks, and ocean life rebounds within their borders. But what kinds of habitats yield the best ecological results? How big must a park be to make a difference on the surrounding areas?

The corridor's tiny reserves are the perfect place to answer these questions. But these trips also serve an equally important outreach role. In Baja, as in most of Mexico, few trust the government, and many view conservation efforts as shadowy conspiracies. But in the corridor each community hears back from fishermen who have worked alongside marine biologists. At night, after grueling days of swimming transects, fishermen, scientists, and government employees hang out together, talking and laughing. Whenever he returns from the research vessel, Rondero says, his community peppers him with questions.

"I have a lifetime of great fishing experiences," he says, sitting on the boat one evening. "I'm proud to be a fisherman. The community has many needs, but we live happily here."

Gazing across the water at the stunning coastline, I ask whether he wants his daughter to marry a fisherman. He pauses and then smiles. "No. I'd like her to be a marine biologist—and do the sort of work I am doing right now." □

---

Erik Vance, a regular contributor, lives in Mexico City and writes frequently about the environment. Thomas P. Peschak photographed the Galápagos Islands for the June 2017 issue of National Geographic.

In Jocotenango, Guatemala, Rosa de Sapeta's family used to avoid her smoke-filled kitchen. But since an aid group helped her replace the open fire with a cleaner burning stove, she says, "I have company while I cook."

| DISPATCHES | GUATEMALA

# When Cooking Kills

Some three billion people around the world cook with open or barely contained fires. The health and environmental consequences can be devastating, especially for women and young children.

BY **MICHELLE NIJHUIS**    PHOTOGRAPHS BY **LYNN JOHNSON**

On Easter Sunday morning, in the small town of San Antonio Aguas Calientes in central Guatemala, Elbia Pérez and her sister, daughters, and 18-month-old grandson are crowded around their kitchen table. On the table, a large pot of tamales, handfuls of spicy meat and corn dough wrapped in plantain leaves, is waiting to be steamed. The room is filled with talk, laughter, and smoke—gritty, eye-watering smoke that provokes deep, scratchy coughs.

The problem isn't that the family lacks a functioning stove. In fact the aluminum-sided kitchen—part of a compound that shelters 45 extended-family members—contains three. But the two-burner gas stove is out of fuel, and the Pérez family can't afford to refill it. Their efficient woodstove, a knee-high concrete cylinder donated by an international aid group, is too small to support the tamale pot. So, as she does about once a month, Pérez has fired up the old wood-burning stove, a brick ruin whose smoke pours directly into the kitchen. Everyone notices the smoke, but it's a familiar annoyance—and compared with the daily challenge of affording food and fuel, it's a minor one.

Some three billion people worldwide cook their food and heat their homes with open or barely contained fires, and while the smoke dissipates quickly, its accumulated costs are steep. The typical cooking fire produces about 400 cigarettes' worth of smoke an hour. In the developing world, health problems from smoke inhalation are a significant cause of death in both children under five and women. To fuel the fires, families can spend 20 hours a week or more gathering wood.

"The first thing we swallowed every morning was smoke," remembers Marco Tulio Guerra, who grew up in rural eastern Guatemala and whose brother was severely burned as a child by the family cooking fire. Household fires also promote deforestation, as trees are felled for firewood. And they're a major source of black carbon— a sunlight-absorbing component of soot that contributes to climate change.

In the 1970s a major earthquake in Guatemala brought international aid groups to the country, where they learned about the costs of open cooking fires. Since then a diffuse network of engineers and philanthropists has invented and distributed hundreds of kinds of improved stoves throughout the developing world, ranging from tiny, gas-powered camping stoves to massive wood-fired ranges. Guerra now owns a factory in central Guatemala that manufactures eight types of improved cookstoves.

Cookstoves, however, are easier to change than human habits. For a new stove to be fully accepted by a household, both stove and fuel must be affordable, accessible, and easy to use—goals that aren't easy to achieve simultaneously. And woe to the cook whose new stove produces food that doesn't measure up. Expedita Ramírez Marroquín, a Guatemalan midwife who works with an international team of environmental health researchers, observes that when it comes to safer cooking methods, critical mothers-in-law often are the highest barriers to change.

Given time, though, even in-laws can adopt new ways. In the western highlands of Guatemala where Ramírez works, great-grandmother Eugenia Velásquez Orozco remembers when her household switched from an open fire to a chimney stove. She missed the direct heat on cold mornings, but she got used to the change.

Now her granddaughter-in-law is learning to use a gas stove. "Give me another five years," Velásquez says with a grin, "and maybe I'll get used to that too." ☐

The Pulitzer Center on Crisis Reporting provided a grant to support this story.

Near Antigua Guatemala, eight-month-old Pablito (above) keeps an eye on breakfast as his mother, Angélica Epatal García, tends the makeshift barrel stove. She and her daughters walk 45 minutes each way to collect the wood for three daily fires. Two years ago Kimberly Galindo (below) was severely burned by her family's open cooking fire. Now 10, she is still undergoing cosmetic surgery for the scars, as well as physical therapy.

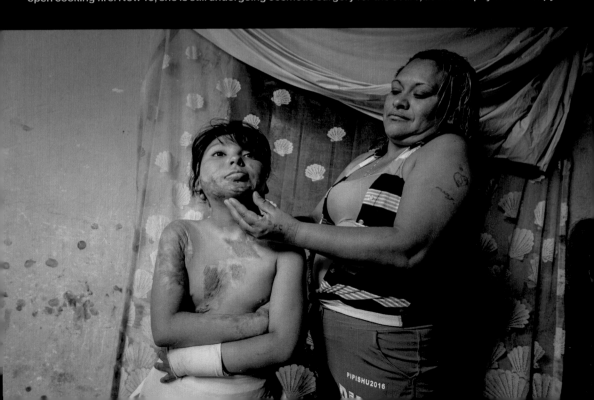

The new yellow stove is efficient, but the old open fire is better for Etelvina Pérez's giant pot in San Antonio Aguas Calientes, where her family of 45 (including Elbia Pérez, see page 78) lives in a cluster of simple rooms. Below: María García Cruz grew up with a gas stove, but she and her husband, Venancio Juárez, can't afford one. "I've never gotten used to this," she says of the smoke. The children have respiratory problems.

A month's worth of propane for the small gas stove costs Rosa Vicente García (above, flanked by her two daughters) and her husband more than two days' work at the Guatemala City landfill, where they scavenge for plastic and metal. Below: Tania López López, seven, plays with her cat in a room whose walls were blackened by an old open fire; the new stove, provided by StoveTeam International, is efficient and safe to touch.

# A tiny country
## Agricultural giant Holland

# feeds the world

## is changing the way we farm.

A sea of greenhouses surrounds a farmer's home in the Westland region of the Netherlands. The Dutch have become world leaders in agricultural innovation, pioneering new paths to fight hunger.

With demand for chicken increasing, Dutch firms are developing technology to maximize poultry production while ensuring humane conditions. This high-tech broiler house holds up to 150,000 birds, from hatching to harvesting.

Furrows of artificial light lend an otherworldly aura to Westland, the greenhouse capital of the Netherlands. Climate-controlled farms such as these grow crops around the clock and in every kind of weather.

The great indoors provides optimal growing conditions for lettuce and other leafy greens at Siberia B.V. Each one of the greenhouse's 22 indoor acres yields as much lettuce as 10 outdoor acres and cuts the need for chemicals by 97 percent.

*By Frank Viviano    Photographs by Luca Locatelli*

In a potato field near the Netherlands' border with Belgium, Dutch farmer Jacob van den Borne is seated in the cabin of an immense harvester before an instrument panel worthy of the starship *Enterprise*.

From his perch 10 feet above the ground, he's monitoring two drones—a driverless tractor roaming the fields and a quadcopter in the air—that provide detailed readings on soil chemistry, water content, nutrients, and growth, measuring the progress of every plant down to the individual potato. Van den Borne's production numbers testify to the power of this "precision farming," as it's known. The global average yield of potatoes per acre is about nine tons. Van den Borne's fields reliably produce more than 20.

That copious output is made all the more remarkable by the other side of the balance sheet: inputs. Almost two decades ago, the Dutch made a national commitment to sustainable agriculture under the rallying cry "Twice as much food using half as many resources." Since 2000, van den Borne and many of his fellow farmers have reduced dependence on water for key crops by as much as 90 percent. They've almost completely eliminated the use of chemical pesticides on plants in greenhouses, and since 2009 Dutch poultry and livestock producers have cut their use of antibiotics by as much as 60 percent.

One more reason to marvel: The Netherlands is a small, densely populated country, with more than 1,300 inhabitants per square mile. It's bereft of almost every resource long thought to be necessary for large-scale agriculture. Yet it's the globe's number two exporter of food as measured by value, second only to the United States, which

Do tomatoes grow best when bathed in LED light from above, beside, or some combination? Plant scientist Henk Kalkman is seeking the answer at the Delphy Improvement Centre in Bleiswijk. Collaboration between academics and entrepreneurs is a key driver of Dutch innovation.

has 270 times its landmass. How on Earth have the Dutch done it?

Seen from the air, the Netherlands resembles no other major food producer—a fragmented patchwork of intensely cultivated fields, most of them tiny by agribusiness standards, punctuated by bustling cities and suburbs. In the country's principal farming regions, there's almost no potato patch, no greenhouse, no hog barn that's out of sight of skyscrapers, manufacturing plants, or urban sprawl. More than half the nation's land area is used for agriculture and horticulture.

Banks of what appear to be gargantuan mirrors stretch across the countryside, glinting when the sun shines and glowing with eerie interior light when night falls. They are Holland's extraordinary greenhouse complexes, some of them covering 175 acres.

These climate-controlled farms enable a country located a scant thousand miles from the Arctic Circle to be a global leader in exports of a fair-weather fruit: the tomato. The Dutch are also the world's top exporter of potatoes and onions and the second largest exporter of vegetables overall in terms of value. More than a third of all global trade in vegetable seeds originates in the Netherlands.

THE BRAIN TRUST behind these astounding numbers is centered at Wageningen University & Research (WUR), located 50 miles southeast of Amsterdam. Widely regarded as the world's top agricultural research institution, WUR is the nodal point of Food Valley, an expansive cluster of agricultural technology start-ups and experimental farms. The name is a deliberate allusion to California's Silicon Valley, with Wageningen emulating the role of Stanford University in its celebrated merger of academia and entrepreneurship.

Ernst van den Ende, managing director of WUR's Plant Sciences Group, embodies Food Valley's blended approach. A renowned scholar with the casual manner of a barista at a hip café, van den Ende is a world authority on plant pathology. But, he says, "I'm not simply a college dean. Half of me runs Plant Sciences, but the other half oversees nine separate business units involved in commercial contract research." Only that mix, "the science-driven in tandem with the market-driven," he maintains, "can meet the challenge that lies ahead."

The challenge? Put in bluntly apocalyptic terms, he says, the planet must produce "more food in the next four decades than all farmers in history have harvested over the past 8,000 years."

That's because by 2050, the Earth will be home to as many as 10 billion people, up from today's 7.5 billion. If massive increases in agricultural yield are not achieved, matched by massive decreases in the use of water and fossil fuels, a billion or more people may face starvation. Hunger could be the 21st century's most urgent problem, and the visionaries working in Food Valley believe they have found innovative solutions. The wherewithal to stave off catastrophic famine is within reach, van den Ende insists. His optimism rests on feedback from more than a thousand WUR projects in more than 140 countries and on its formal pacts with governments and universities on six continents to share advances and implement them.

A conversation with van den Ende is a white-knuckle ride on a torrent of brainstorms, statistics, and predictions. African drought? "Water isn't the fundamental problem. It's poor soil," he says. "The absence of nutrients can be offset by cultivating plants that act in symbiosis with certain bacteria to produce their own fertilizer." The soaring cost of grain to feed animals? "Feed them grasshoppers instead," he says. One hectare of land yields one metric ton of soy protein, a common livestock feed, a year. The same amount of land can produce 150 tons of insect protein.

The conversation rushes on to the use of LED lighting to permit 24-hour cultivation in precisely climate-controlled greenhouses. It then detours to a misconception that sustainable agriculture means minimal human intervention in nature.

"Look at the island of Bali!" he exclaims. For at least a thousand years, its farmers have raised ducks and fish within the same flooded paddies where rice is cultivated. It's an entirely self-contained food system, irrigated by intricate canal systems along mountain terraces sculpted by human hands.

"There's your model of sustainability," van den Ende says.

AT EVERY TURN in the Netherlands, the future of sustainable agriculture is taking shape—not in the boardrooms of big corporations but on thousands of modest family farms. You see it vividly in the terrestrial paradise of Ted Duijvestijn and his brothers Peter, Ronald, and Remco. Like the Balinese, the Duijvestijns have constructed a self-contained food system in which a near-perfect balance prevails between human ingenuity and nature's potential.

At the Duijvestijns' 36-acre greenhouse complex near the old city of Delft, visitors stroll among ranks of deep green tomato vines, 20 feet tall. Rooted not in soil but in fibers spun from

# Punching above its weight

The tiny Netherlands has become an agricultural powerhouse – the second largest global exporter of food by dollar value after the U.S. – with only a fraction of the land available to other countries. How has it achieved this? By using the world's most efficient agricultural technologies.

## Harvesting impressive yields

Over the past three decades, the Dutch tomato industry has become the world leader in yield, producing more tomatoes per square mile than anywhere else in the world.

*Yield*
**No. 1 globally**
144,352 tons
per square mile

*Area harvested
for tomatoes*
**No. 95 globally**
6.9 square miles

**Netherlands**

## Growing under glass

Dutch horticulture relies heavily on greenhouses, allowing farmers to closely control growing conditions and use fewer resources like water and fertilizer.

1 mile

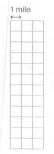

**Change from 2003-2014**

| Vegetable production | ▲28% |
| Energy used* | ▼ 6% |
| Pesticides | ▼ 9% |
| Fertilizer | ▼29% |

Greenhouses in Netherlands
**36**
square miles

Area of Manhattan
**23**
square miles

*Latest available data (2012)

The Netherlands enjoys high yields in multiple staple crops in addition to tomatoes.

**Top 25 producers by yield, 2014** *in tons per square mile*

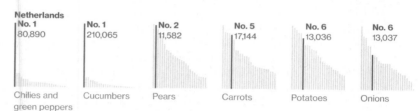

**Netherlands**
| **No. 1** | **No. 1** | **No. 2** | **No. 5** | **No. 6** | **No. 6** |
| 80,890 | 210,065 | 11,582 | 17,144 | 13,036 | 13,037 |

Chilies and green peppers | Cucumbers | Pears | Carrots | Potatoes | Onions

**Top 25 tomato producers, 2014**
*ranked by yield*

The U.S. ranks third in both tomato production and yield.

China uses more land to farm tomatoes than any other country, making it the world leader in production despite average yields per square mile.

Nigeria has the third largest area harvested for tomatoes, but the lowest yield among the top 25 producers.

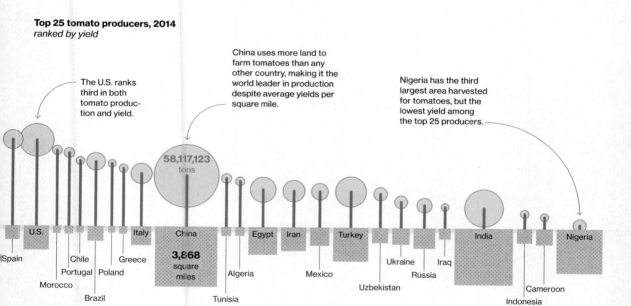

58,117,123 tons

China
3,868 square miles

Spain | U.S. | Chile | Portugal | Poland | Greece | Italy | China | Algeria | Egypt | Iran | Mexico | Turkey | Uzbekistan | Ukraine | Russia | Iraq | India | Indonesia | Cameroon | Nigeria

Morocco | Brazil | Tunisia

## Doing more with less

Utilizing innovations on a large scale, like hydroponic farming – growing plants without soil in nutrient-rich solutions – reduces runoff, saving both water and money.

**Total water footprint of tomato production**
*Gallons per pound, 2010*

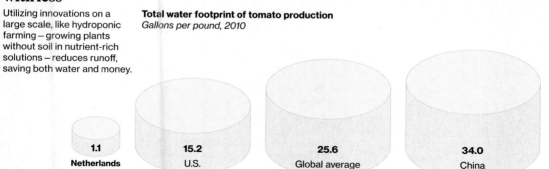

| 1.1 | 15.2 | 25.6 | 34.0 |
| **Netherlands** | U.S. | Global average | China |

JASON TREAT, NGM STAFF; KELSEY NOWAKOWSKI. SOURCES: FAOSTAT; ARJEN HOEKSTRA, UNIVERSITY OF TWENTE; STATISTICS NETHERLANDS (CBS)

Jan and Gijs van den Borne play on mountains of potatoes grown on their family's ultra-productive farm, which yields twice the global average. The reason? Drones and other tools assess the health of individual plants and determine exactly how much water and nutrients they need to thrive.

A rotary milking machine enables one operator to milk up to 150 cows an hour at Wageningen University's Dairy Campus, where researchers seek to address the challenges posed by dairy farming in the densely populated Netherlands.

basalt and chalk, the plants are heavy with tomatoes—15 varieties in all—to suit the taste of the most demanding palate. In 2015 an international jury of horticultural experts named the Duijvestijns the world's most innovative tomato growers.

Since relocating and restructuring their 70-year-old farm in 2004, the Duijvestijns have declared resource independence on every front. The farm produces almost all of its own energy and fertilizer and even some of the packaging materials necessary for the crop's distribution and sale. The growing environment is kept at optimal temperatures year-round by heat generated from geothermal aquifers that simmer under at least half of the Netherlands.

The only irrigation source is rainwater, says Ted, who manages the cultivation program. Each kilogram of tomatoes from his fiber-rooted plants requires less than four gallons of water, compared with 16 gallons for plants in open fields. Once each year the entire crop is regrown from seeds, and the old vines are processed to make packaging crates. The few pests that manage to enter the Duijvestijn greenhouses are greeted by a ravenous army of defenders such as the fierce *Phytoseiulus persimilis,* a predatory mite that shows no interest in tomatoes but gorges itself on hundreds of destructive spider mites.

A few days before I visited the Duijvestijns' operation, Ted had attended a meeting of farmers and researchers at Wageningen. "This is how we come up with innovative ways to move ahead, to keep improving," he told me. "People from all over Holland get together to discuss different perspectives and common goals. No one knows all the answers on their own."

THE SEARCH FOR ANSWERS to a life-or-death question gave rise to one of the Netherlands' most innovative companies. Half a century ago, Jan Koppert was growing cucumbers on his land and using toxic chemical sprays to fend off pests. When a physician declared him allergic to pesticides, Koppert set out to learn all he could about the natural enemies of insects and arachnids.

Today Koppert Biological Systems is the global

Tomato grower Jasper Oussoren checks a generator that converts natural gas into electricity for lighting. By-products – heat and $CO_2$ – are captured and used to warm greenhouses and boost plant growth.

pacesetter in biological pest and disease control, with 1,330 employees and 26 international subsidiaries marketing its products in 96 countries. Koppert's firm can provide you with cotton bags of ladybug larvae that mature into voracious consumers of aphids. Or how about a bottle containing 2,000 of those predatory mites that hunt down spider mites on plants and suck them dry? Or a box of 500 million nematodes that mount deadly assaults on fly larvae that prey on commercial mushrooms?

Koppert's legions make love as well as war, in the guise of enthusiastic bumblebees. No form of artificial pollination matches the efficiency of bees buzzing from flower to flower, gathering nectar to nourish their queen and helping to fertilize the ovaries of plants along the way. Each Koppert hive accounts for daily visits to half a million flowers. Farmers using the bees

typically report 20 to 30 percent increases in yields and fruit weight, for less than half the cost of artificial pollination.

NOWHERE IS THE NETHERLANDS' agricultural technology more cutting-edge than in the embryonic organism in which most food is literally rooted: seeds. And nowhere are the controversies that surround the future of agriculture more heated. Chief among them is the development of genetically modified organisms to produce larger and more pest-resistant crops. To their critics, GMOs conjure up a Frankenstein scenario, fraught with uncertainty about the consequences of radical experimentation with living entities.

Dutch firms are among the world leaders in the seed business, with close to $1.7 billion worth of exports in 2016. Yet they market no GMO products. A new seed variety in Europe's heavily regulated GMO arena can cost a hundred million dollars and require 12 to 14 years of research and development, according to KeyGene's Arjen van Tunen. By contrast, the latest achievements in the venerable science of molecular breeding—which introduces no foreign genes—can deliver remarkable gains in five to 10 years, with development costs as low as $100,000 and seldom more than a million dollars. It is a direct descendant of methods employed by farmers in the Fertile Crescent 10,000 years ago.

The sales catalog of Rijk Zwaan, another Dutch breeder, offers high-yield seeds in more than 25 broad groups of vegetables, many that defend themselves naturally against major pests. Heleen Bos is responsible for the company's organic accounts and international development projects. She might be expected to dwell on the fact that a single high-tech Rijk Zwaan greenhouse tomato seed, priced below $0.50, has been known to produce a mind-boggling 150 pounds of tomatoes. Instead she talks about the hundreds of millions of people, most of them women and children, who lack sufficient food.

Like many of the entrepreneurs at Food Valley firms, Bos has worked in the fields and cities of the world's poorest nations. With lengthy postings to Mozambique, Nicaragua, and Bangladesh over the past 30 years, she knows that hunger and devastating famine are not abstract threats.

"Of course, we can't immediately implement the kind of ultrahigh-tech agriculture over there that you see in the Netherlands," she says. "But we are well into introducing medium-tech solutions that can make a huge difference." She cites the proliferation of relatively inexpensive plastic greenhouses that have tripled some crop yields compared with those of open fields, where crops are more subject to pests and drought.

Since 2008 Rijk Zwaan has supported a breeding program in Tanzania at a 50-acre trial field in the shadow of Mount Kilimanjaro. Its seeds are sent to Holland for quality control tests on germination rates, purity, and resistance to pests and diseases. Collaborative projects are under way in Kenya, Peru, and Guatemala. "We try to develop seeds for their specific conditions," Bos says. But the starting point, she adds emphatically, cannot be the sort of top-down approach that has doomed many well-meaning foreign aid projects.

"We have constant, tremendously important conversations with the small growers themselves—on their needs, on the weather and soil conditions they face, on costs," she says.

FOR SOME DUTCH RESEARCHERS, concern for people threatened by hunger stems in part from a national trauma: The Netherlands was the last Western country to suffer a serious famine, when 10,000 to 20,000 people died in German-occupied lands during the final year of World War II. Decades later, WUR's Rudy Rabbinge, professor emeritus of sustainable development and food security, took up the cause when he helped devise extensive changes in the faculty, student body,

# Spreading the word, feeding the world

Wageningen University & Research, nestled in Food Valley – the Dutch agro-tech version of Silicon Valley – is key to the Netherlands' agricultural success. The university is also exporting their innovative approach around the globe.

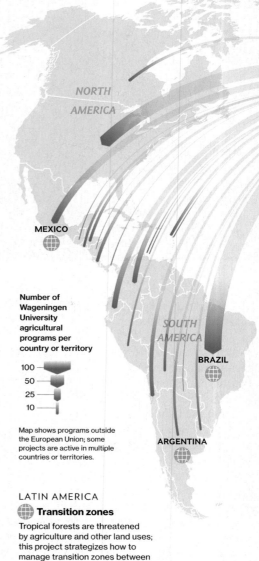

Number of Wageningen University agricultural programs per country or territory

100
50
25
10

Map shows programs outside the European Union; some projects are active in multiple countries or territories.

LATIN AMERICA
Transition zones

Tropical forests are threatened by agriculture and other land uses; this project strategizes how to manage transition zones between farm and forest.

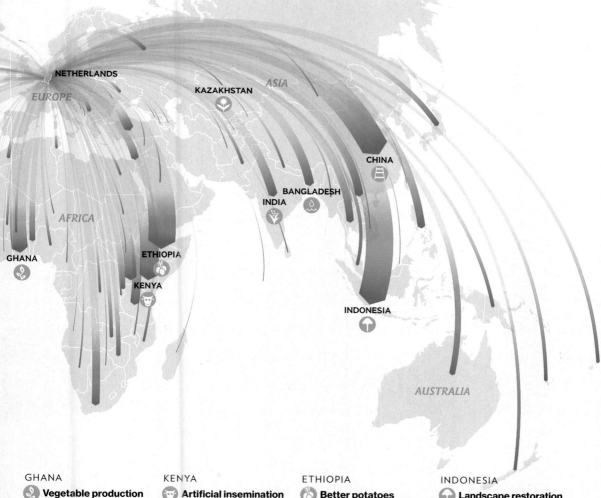

## KAZAKHSTAN
 **Dandelion rubber**

The rubber industry contributes to deforestation in Asia; this project seeks to develop natural rubber from the roots of dandelions.

## INDIA
 **Rice innovation**

Labor-intensive, low-water rice cultivation has increased yields in recent decades; this project studies how agricultural policy can spur further innovation.

## BANGLADESH
 **Water quality**

Climate change has led to more frequent and intense flooding; this project studies the resulting spread of waterborne pathogens.

## CHINA
**Safe transportation**

A new railway from Rotterdam to Chongqing traverses extreme seasonal heat and cold; this project aims to ensure food safety en route.

## GHANA
 **Vegetable production**

The GhanaVeg project aims to develop a sustainable and competitive market for vegetables, to meet the rising demand of a growing middle class.

## KENYA
 **Artificial insemination**

Small dairy breeders have limited access to AI services and quality heifers; this project studies how better access could improve food security.

## ETHIOPIA
 **Better potatoes**

Yields here are low for root and tuber crops; this project aims to improve seed-tuber quality and analyze the economic consequences of that change.

## INDONESIA
 **Landscape restoration**

Forests are being destroyed by development and farming; this project works with private and public interests to optimize sustainable business models.

JASON TREAT, NGM STAFF; KELSEY NOWAKOWSKI. SOURCE: WAGENINGEN UNIVERSITY & RESEARCH

Knowledge is the Netherlands' most valuable export, say instructors and students at Wageningen University & Research (WUR), where half of all graduate students hail from other countries — some threatened by recurring famine.

Ruud Veloo monitors an experimental "photobioreactor" at WUR's AlgaePARC. Light fuels the growth of microalgae, which are used to produce proteins and lipids, the basis of many food chains.

and curriculum that transformed the institution into what he calls "a university for the world, and not simply for the Dutch." Today a hefty share of the academic and research activities at WUR are focused on problems facing poor nations.

Some 45 percent of its graduate students—including nearly two-thirds of all Ph.D. candidates—are recruited abroad, representing more than a hundred nations. Asians, led by Chinese and Indonesians, outnumber almost all non-Dutch Europeans combined. WUR alumni are found in the highest echelons of agricultural ministries across Africa, Asia, and Latin America.

In a campus cafeteria, I sit down with three of WUR's most promising students, a description that, not long ago, would have meant male and Dutch born. All three are young women, hailing from Uganda, Nepal, and Indonesia.

"I met a Wageningen alumna when I was an undergrad in Uganda," Leah Nandudu tells me when I ask how she wound up here. "She was an expert on phenotyping," the advanced studies that paint a detailed portrait of a plant's traits and potential. "It inspired me to discover that an African could do these things. She was the future; she was where we need to go."

The meeting eventually led Nandudu to a WUR scholarship. Her father farms three acres, split between coffee and bananas. Her mother teaches English in a primary school and helps in the field. "We have all the problems farmers face everywhere today, only much worse, especially due to the consequences of climate change."

Pragya Shrestha was raised in the Nepali countryside, some parts of which have been wracked by years of reliance on pesticides and fertilizers. Sounder, sustainable methods have made few inroads so far.

"It's a political problem," she says. New cultivation methods can't be implemented because of a shortage of public funding. "It's also a population problem, the fragmentation of the land into smaller and smaller parcels, suitable only for the use of inefficient human labor and generating very little income."

Renna Eliana Warjoto is from Bandung, the third largest city in Indonesia. "People are

A farm atop a former factory in The Hague produces vegetables and fish in a self-sustaining loop: Fish waste fertilizes plants, which filter the water for the fish. Local restaurants proudly offer the veggies and "city swimmers."

mistrustful of ideas that come from abroad," she says, as Shrestha and Nandudu nod in agreement. "Farmers are so used to having marginal lives and incomes," she adds, "that they have a hard time believing things could be different."

In 1944-45 a lethal famine struck the island of Java, where Bandung is located, killing some 2.4 million people. Devastating regional crop failures have haunted Indonesia as recently as 2005. Food supplies periodically run out in rural Nepal because of drought and high prices on essential imports. In 2011 a famine in the Horn of Africa affected 13 million people, and in 2017 1.6 million Ugandans face starvation without rapid assistance from abroad. All these events were unimaginable at the time, yet they pale in comparison to what could lie ahead. The number of people menaced by famine in just three African nations and across the Red Sea in Yemen

exceeds 20 million today and is rising inexorably, according to the United Nations. "We are facing the largest humanitarian crisis since the creation of the UN," the organization's emergency relief coordinator, Stephen O'Brien, warned in March.

"Our most difficult task is changing the perceptions of our own people—about the crisis we confront and what we must do to address it," Nandudu says. "That's my job when I go home. We cannot turn our faces away from reality."

SOME 4,000 MILES south of Wageningen, in a family-owned bean field in Africa's Eastern Rift Valley, a team from SoilCares, a Dutch agricultural technology firm, explains the functions of a small handheld device. In conjunction with a cell phone app, the device analyzes the soil's pH, organic matter, and other properties, then uploads the results to a database in the Netherlands and

returns a detailed report on optimal fertilizer use and nutrient needs—all in less than 10 minutes. At a cost of a few dollars, the report provides input that can help reduce crop losses by enormous margins to farmers who have never had access to soil sampling of any kind.

Less than 5 percent of the world's estimated 570 million farms have access to a soil lab. That's the kind of number the Dutch see as a challenge.

"What does our work mean for developing countries? That question is always raised here," says Martin Scholten, who directs WUR's Animal Sciences Group. "It's part of every conversation." □

---

**Frank Viviano**, a foreign correspondent based in Italy, has covered stories in Europe, Asia, Latin America, and Africa. **Luca Locatelli** specializes in photographing interactions between people and technology.

Fossey devoted almost 20 years to her studies before she was murdered in 1985. She developed close relationships with some animals, including these rescued orphans, named Coco and Pucker.

# The Gorillas Dian Fossey Saved

To some in Rwanda she was a menacing intruder, but her work kept mountain gorillas from being wiped out. Today the great apes face new challenges.

Had Fossey not so fiercely protected the gorillas and their habitat, these apes, resting on the high-elevation slopes of Mount Karisimbi, probably wouldn't exist today. But her methods earned her the enmity of many locals.

**WATCH** ON NATIONAL GEOGRAPHIC

*Dian Fossey: Secrets in the Mist,* a three-hour series, tells the story of the life, work, murder, and legacy of the gorilla researcher. Premieres later this year.

*By Elizabeth Royte*
*Photographs by Ronan Donovan*

**S**hortly after dawn two mountain gorillas swing gracefully over the shoulder-high stone wall that borders Volcanoes National Park in northwestern Rwanda. Landing lightly on cropped grass, the silverbacks stroll downhill through cultivated fields—knuckle-walking at first, then upright on two legs. The adult males belly up to eucalyptus trees and score the bark with their incisors. Then, joined by females and juveniles from their group, which researchers call Titus, they advance on a spindly stand of bamboo.

Later that morning Veronica Vecellio, the gorilla program manager for the Dian Fossey Gorilla Fund International, settles onto a log inside the park, high on a thickly forested, mist-shrouded slope of the Virunga Mountains, and turns her attention to a silverback known as Urwibutso. A frequent wall hopper, Urwibutso is carefully folding thistle leaves before placing them in his mouth. When he turns toward Vecellio, an ebullient woman who studies gorilla group dynamics, she snaps a picture, then zooms in on a wound on his nose.

"He fought with another silverback from Titus this morning," she whispers intently. (Silverbacks get their name from the white hairs that blanket males, saddlelike, when they reach maturity.)

The Titus group has been sneaking over the park wall for 10 years, Vecellio says, and each year it ventures farther. The situation isn't ideal. Gorillas don't eat the potatoes or beans that villagers plant—not yet. But they do kill trees, a valuable resource, and come into close contact with human and livestock waste, which is loaded with pathogens. The potential for disease spillover between species is high, and the chance gorillas could survive a virulent outbreak is low. So when the Titus group gets within a stone's throw of the mud-and-stick homes of Bisate, a village of about 10,000 people, park guards waving bamboo poles slowly shoo them back uphill. Vecellio sighs. "This is the price we're paying for success."

DIAN FOSSEY, AN AMERICAN with no experience researching wild animals, arrived in Africa to study mountain gorillas in the late 1960s at the urging of anthropologist Louis Leakey and with financing from the National Geographic Society. By 1973 the population of these great apes in the Virunga Mountains had fallen below 275, but today, thanks to extreme conservation measures—constant monitoring, intensive antipoaching efforts, and emergency veterinary interventions—there are now about 480.

More gorillas have been a boon for genetic diversity: For years, researchers have documented evidence of inbreeding, such as cleft palates and webbed fingers and toes. But the population

**For more than a decade Fossey lived alone in a remote and damp cabin in an outpost she built between two mountains, boiling water for baths, eating food from cans, and reading and writing by lantern light.**

uptick has a downside. "Group sizes are larger," Vecellio says. The Pablo group hit 65 members in 2006; it's now down to about 25—still almost three times as large as average gorilla groups in the Virunga Mountains in Uganda and the Democratic Republic of the Congo. "The density of groups in certain areas is also up," Vecellio adds.

Clashes between groups, which raise the odds gorillas will suffer injuries or commit infanticide to wipe out a competing male's genes, are six times as frequent now as 10 years ago. "We're seeing an increase in the level of stress too," Vecellio says, and possibly increased exposure to stress-related diseases.

These problems would not be so acute if the

mountain gorillas had unlimited room to roam. But Volcanoes National Park is just 62 square miles, and a rising sea of humanity, hungry for more farm and grazing land, laps at its boundary. Villagers routinely flout park rules and clamber over the stone wall to cut firewood, hunt meat, gather honey, and in the dry season, collect water.

From the morning's eucalyptus and bamboo raid, it's obvious the Titus group is comfortable outside the forest. But the gorillas have little immunity to human diseases, and their blasé attitude toward people leaves them vulnerable.

Such dynamics are largely hidden to the park's visitors. Researchers who study Rwanda's mountain gorillas, however, understand that they're

Fossey, wearing a skull mask in this photo shot in 1969, took advantage of herders' beliefs in sorcery to try to frighten them and their cattle from the forest. She also demolished traps, beat poachers with stinging nettles, and raided their camps.

as in Fossey's day, a profusion of ferns, vines, and grasses seems to tint the humid air green, and a stream flows past the clearing. When the corpse of an infant gorilla disappeared, Fossey spent countless hours hunched on this stream bank examining adult dung for irrefutable evidence of cannibalism, but she never found it.

After an intruder murdered Fossey in her bed in 1985—a crime that remains a mystery—researchers continued to work at Karisoke. The camp shut down in 1994 during the Rwandan genocide, and rebels traversing the forest ransacked it. Today the much expanded Karisoke Research Center operates out of a modern office building in nearby Musanze, and the only man-made traces of Fossey's site are foundation stones and the occasional stovepipe.

Despite the climb, drenching rains, and temperatures that can drop into the 30s, some 500 pilgrims a year trek to Karisoke to pay tribute to Fossey. Many know her from her book *Gorillas in the Mist,* which inspired the 1988 movie. On my visit, though, I have the place mostly to myself. As I explore the grounds, trying to imagine Fossey's life here, porters quietly scrape lichen from the wooden signs that mark the graves of 25 gorillas. Just outside this rustic cemetery, a bronze plaque rises over Fossey herself.

The tall, outspoken Fossey was not universally beloved. Many locals considered her an interloper or a witch, who not only confounded cultural norms but also presented an existential threat to those who depended on the forest for sustenance. From the start, Fossey made clear her priorities. She chased herders and their cattle out of the park: The animals trampled the plants that gorillas favored and forced them upslope to temperatures they couldn't withstand. Every year she destroyed thousands of traps and snares intended to catch antelope and buffalo. The snares didn't kill gorillas outright but often

documenting a unique moment—not only the increase in population of a critically endangered species but also the possible revision of the rules assumed to govern its social behavior.

ON AN OVERCAST MORNING, with temperatures in the mid-50s, it takes me nearly two hours to hike from the outskirts of Bisate through calf-deep mud and shoulder-high nettles to the research site established in 1967 by Fossey in the high-elevation saddle between Mounts Karisimbi and Visoke. The camp, which Fossey named Karisoke, began with two tents and grew to include more than a dozen cabins and outbuildings in a grove of moss-shrouded Hagenia trees, 80 feet tall. Today,

# The Gorillas of Karisoke

In 1967 Dian Fossey set up a camp she called Karisoke in the Virunga Mountains, where she began studying several dozen gorillas. Fifty years later, the Dian Fossey Gorilla Fund International continues her work. It has observed more than 350 apes, making the population one of the most intensely researched.

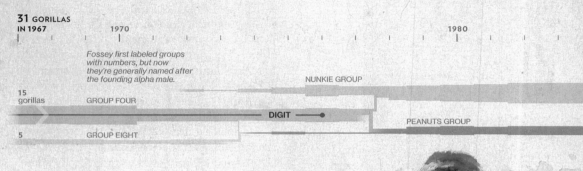

**31** GORILLAS
IN 1967

1970

1980

Fossey first labeled groups with numbers, but now they're generally named after the founding alpha male.

NUNKIE GROUP

15 gorillas

GROUP FOUR

DIGIT

PEANUTS GROUP

5

GROUP EIGHT

## FIVE DECADES OF GROWTH

Here are the trajectories of the primary groups and some key gorillas that Fossey studied. Groups typically split after the deaths of alpha males or disputes over dominance, with a new male luring away females to start another group.

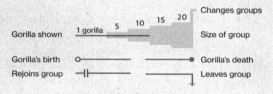

Changes groups

1 gorilla 5 10 15 20

Gorilla shown

Size of group

Gorilla's birth — Gorilla's death

Rejoins group — Leaves group

**DIGIT | Fossey's favorite**
Digit was killed by poachers in 1977 while defending Group Four. The death of the famed gorilla was announced on CBS News.

11 GROUP FIVE

POPPY CANTSBEE MAGGIE

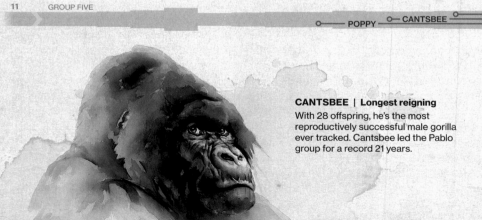

**CANTSBEE | Longest reigning**
With 28 offspring, he's the most reproductively successful male gorilla ever tracked. Cantsbee led the Pablo group for a record 21 years.

1970 - Fossey appears on the cover of *National Geographic* magazine, which features an article she wrote on her work.

1977 - After Digit is killed, Fossey starts weekly antipoaching patrols and, in 1978, the nonprofit Digit Fund to protect and monitor gorillas.

1981 - A thorough census of the gorilla population, the first full census undertaken since 1973, counts 240 apes.

*Data as of June 2017. Data are not shown for gorillas monitored briefly. Group populations are tallied at the end of each year.

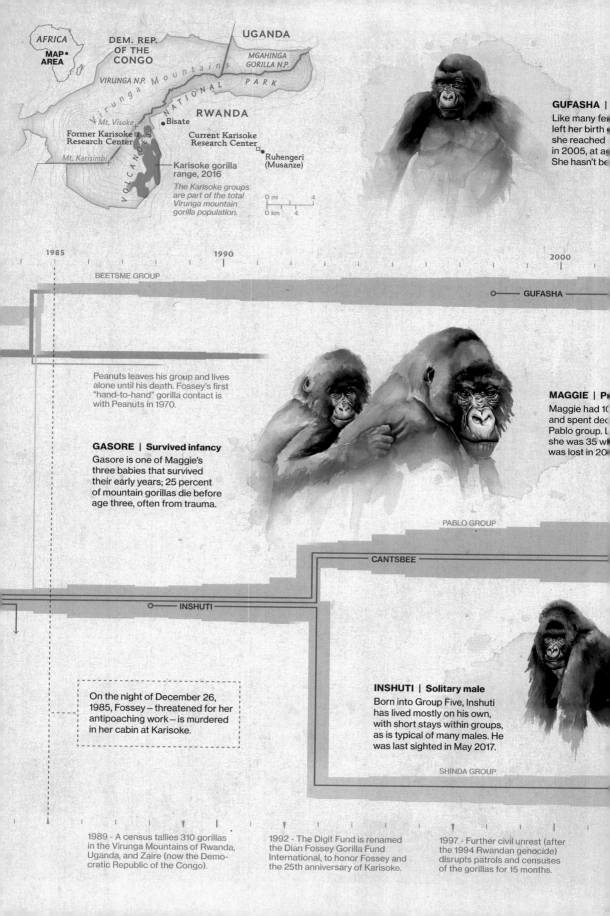

**AFRICA**
**MAP·AREA**

**DEM. REP. OF THE CONGO**

**UGANDA**

**VIRUNGA N.P.**

*Virunga Mountains*

**MGAHINGA GORILLA N.P.**

**NATIONAL PARK**

**RWANDA**

Bisate

**VOLCANOES**

*Mt. Visoke*

Former Karisoke Research Center

Current Karisoke Research Center

*Mt. Karisimbi*

Ruhengeri (Musanze)

Karisoke gorilla range, 2016

*The Karisoke groups are part of the total Virunga mountain gorilla population.*

0 mi      4
0 km     4

**GUFASHA |**
Like many fe...
left her birth ...
she reached
in 2005, at ag...
She hasn't be...

1985          1990                              2000

BEETSME GROUP

GUFASHA

Peanuts leaves his group and lives alone until his death. Fossey's first "hand-to-hand" gorilla contact is with Peanuts in 1970.

**GASORE | Survived infancy**
Gasore is one of Maggie's three babies that survived their early years; 25 percent of mountain gorillas die before age three, often from trauma.

**MAGGIE | Pr...**
Maggie had 10...
and spent dec...
Pablo group. L...
she was 35 wh...
was lost in 20...

PABLO GROUP

CANTSBEE

INSHUTI

On the night of December 26, 1985, Fossey — threatened for her antipoaching work — is murdered in her cabin at Karisoke.

**INSHUTI | Solitary male**
Born into Group Five, Inshuti has lived mostly on his own, with short stays within groups, as is typical of many males. He was last sighted in May 2017.

SHINDA GROUP

1989 - A census tallies 310 gorillas in the Virunga Mountains of Rwanda, Uganda, and Zaire (now the Democratic Republic of the Congo).

1992 - The Digit Fund is renamed the Dian Fossey Gorilla Fund International, to honor Fossey and the 25th anniversary of Karisoke.

1997 - Further civil unrest (after the 1994 Rwandan genocide) disrupts patrols and censuses of the gorillas for 15 months.

**POPPY | Returned home**
At 41, Poppy is the oldest gorilla tracked by the Fossey Fund. Born under Fossey's watch, she left the Karisoke population in 1984 but rejoined it 30 years later.

**113** GORILLAS IN 2017*

...ost female
...les, Gufasha
...oup when
...xual maturity —
...seven.
...seen since.

...lific mother
...offspring
...des in the
...er solitary,
...n her trail

2010

IYAMBERE GROUP    5
POPPY

TITUS GROUP    8

KURYAMA GROUP    8

ISABUKURU GROUP    15
GASORE

BWENGE GROUP   GASORE

32

MAGGIE

In 2007 three large, multi-male gorilla groups split to form eight separate groups. Females also begin transferring between groups at four times the rate of the previous four decades.

MUSILIKALE GROUP   13

INSHUTI GROUP   INSHUTI

MAFUNZO GROUP   12

UGENDA GROUP

URUGAMBA GROUP

GIRANEZA GROUP   5

NTAMBARA GROUP   9

2006 - The Pablo group, the largest ever recorded, reaches a new high with 65 gorillas, six times the average group size.

2010 - Conservation measures have helped the Virunga gorilla population double to 480 since the 1980s.

2016 - As the Karisoke population grows, new groups compete for space and expand their ranges into higher and colder altitudes.

DANIELA SANTAMARINA AND LAUREN C. TIERNEY, NGM STAFF; MEG ROOSEVELT. ART: CHARITY OETGEN
SOURCE: TARA STOINSKI, DIAN FOSSEY GORILLA FUND INTERNATIONAL

## Then and now

Researchers identify gorillas by their distinctive noseprints. Digit (above), an intimidating silverback and a Fossey favorite, became the namesake of her campaign to raise money after he was killed. In April trackers with the Dian Fossey Gorilla Fund International found Fasha (below), a juvenile, entangled in a snare. Veterinarians with Gorilla Doctors removed the trap, likely saving his life.

DIAN FOSSEY, NATIONAL GEOGRAPHIC CREATIVE (ABOVE)

# New challenges

Farmers from Bisate village near Volcanoes National Park have become inured to mountain gorillas leaving the forest to feed on bamboo, planted as building material. Sometimes gorillas from the Titus group even sleep outside the park, increasing their risk of contracting a deadly disease from humans or livestock.

## Fossey showed the world affectionate gorillas, while her own life was filled with bitterness.

pinched off limbs that became gangrenous or fatally infected. Fossey captured and beat poachers with stinging nettles, burned down their huts, confiscated their weapons, and once even took a poacher's child hostage. But her most effective tactic—and an enduring part of her legacy—was paying locals to patrol the park and insisting that Rwandan authorities enforce antipoaching laws. Fossey was a polarizing figure, but as Jane Goodall, the chimpanzee expert, once said, "If Dian had not been there, probably there might have been no mountain gorillas in Rwanda today."

Contemplating the simple plaque on Fossey's headstone, I'm struck by all that was extraordinary about this pioneer: her 18 years in the forest, her epic battles for funding, and her struggles for academic legitimacy, physical health, and emotional connection. It's beyond irony that Fossey showed the world a largely peaceable realm of affectionate gorilla families, while her own life was characterized by bitterness and mistrust. "She was alone and hated by many," says Vecellio, who describes herself as a lifelong Fossey "superfan."

Fossey's grave lies just a few steps from that of Digit, the silverback whom she reluctantly turned into a fund-raising bonanza—by creating the Digit Fund—after he was stabbed and decapitated by poachers. Fossey was desperate for money to pay her trackers and antipoaching teams. But she hated the idea of generating revenue from ecotourism, and she considered gorilla tourists—who began arriving at Karisoke, against her wishes, in 1979—a driver of gorilla extinction. And yet it was Fossey's knack for publicizing her studies through lectures and articles that turned the gorillas into causes célèbres. It was also Fossey who figured out how to habituate gorillas to humans, without which the tourist trade wouldn't exist.

Rwanda barely tolerated Fossey when she was alive—authorities repeatedly denied her visa applications and stymied her efforts to halt poaching. But the country was quick to realize that her death and burial within a national park, Vecellio says, "had enormous symbolic value. It created a sense of urgency and brought international support for gorilla conservation." Last year more than 30,000 people hiked into the park, each paying the Rwanda Development Board, which oversees the nation's tourism, $750 for a gorilla-group encounter limited to one hour. The fees, which recently jumped to $1,500, pay for security and monitoring, and they ensure the government's commitment to protecting the species.

For the safety of animals and humans, the development board allows only eight people in each trekking group. But with more groups of gorillas, more visitors than ever can have their primal moment. Higher visitation means more money is funneled, through a revenue-sharing plan, into local communities, and it creates ripple opportunities for businesses. During the high season, tourists fill more than 20 hotels and guesthouses in and around Musanze—the town had just one when Fossey arrived—generating income for drivers, housekeepers, waiters, chefs, bartenders, guards, farmers, park guides, porters, and trackers.

Tourism opportunities may expand even more. The Rwandan government, in collaboration with the Massachusetts Institute of Technology, is considering the construction of a climate research station on the summit of Mount Karisimbi, at 14,787 feet. A cable car would whisk scientists to their instruments and tourists to crater-top zip lines. Worried that the project could destroy gorilla habitat, conservation groups are calling for a comprehensive study of its environmental impacts.

IT'S LATE MORNING before my guide locates the Sabyinyo group, a short hike from the park boundary, through a dim bamboo forest. As the rain that has been pelting lets up, we hear the animals—stripping and munching the scenery—well before we spot them. A mountain of muscle, the silverback Gihishamwotsi sits in a clearing of crushed ferns and giant lobelias, calmly overseeing a harem of females and their babies. Now and then he grunts, eliciting guttural responses from gorillas just out of sight. When he rises suddenly to beat his chest, he gets more of a reaction—alarm—from me than from anyone else.

I'd suspected that a lifetime of watching nature documentaries and knowing that gorillas and humans share 98 percent of their DNA would diminish the thrill of seeing these animals in the flesh. But from six feet away, I'm dumbstruck by that flesh: the babies' feet, as smooth and meaty as yams, the mothers' kielbasa-size fingers, the silverback's forearms, which resemble muffs fit for giants. I'm entranced too by the familiarity of their gestures: Like us, they scratch! They play with their toes! They hug their babies to their faces! On the heels of this epiphany, however, comes guilt—for intruding upon their privacy.

When my hour is up, I dash down the mountain to meet Winnie Eckardt in a small room in the Karisoke Research Center. Leaning against a freezer, the research manager gestures to the trove of frozen samples at her back. "Welcome to the poop lab," she says with a grin. Eckardt, who jumps at any chance to summit the nearby volcanoes, has been studying mountain gorillas since 2004 and now supervises the monthly collection and processing of fecal samples—which contain hormones, enzymes, and DNA, in addition to viruses and parasites—from 130 animals. (Disposable bags are a key component of ranger gear.)

"Wildlife endocrinology is an increasingly significant field," Eckardt says, "and it's a very powerful tool." Karisoke researchers are extracting from gorilla feces the stress hormone cortisol and correlating it with observed interactions. "Now we can say this or that type of interaction is causing stress," she says.

In 2014 researchers compared observations on demographics and behavior in gorilla groups with genetic analyses of DNA extracted from fecal samples. Their results shed light on key differences between how far males and females disperse from their natal group—one of the main factors that determine a population's genetic structure.

DNA sequencing is also telling researchers about gorilla paternity. "From these studies we've learned that the dominant silverback is the father of most babies in a group but not all," Eckardt says. The number two and three silverbacks are also passing on their genes. This raises more interesting questions: How do nondominant silverbacks decide whether to stay in a group or to try to seduce females into establishing a new group? What factors are linked with reproductive success? How do you stay number one? "There is a lot of competition out there," Eckardt notes.

By revealing evidence of inbreeding and the success of various family lineages, DNA analysis also informs conservation decisions. "If managers can save only a few groups of gorillas," Eckardt says, "you want to choose groups that are distantly related. If they're inbred, they won't behave normally or may have health complications, which you may need to monitor differently." Less genetic diversity also means gorillas are more vulnerable to disease and to climate-change disruptions.

RESEARCHERS HAVE PUBLISHED nearly 300 papers based on data collected at Karisoke, but there's still much to learn. "If you'd done a study from 1997 till 2007, which is a long study," says Tara Stoinski, president and chief scientific officer of the Fossey Fund, "you'd think there was no infanticide here. But we know, from before and after that period, that it's not an uncommon behavior."

Through the 1970s gorillas lived at low densities with a lot of human disturbance—like poaching and cattle herding—which shattered groups and drove lone males to lure females from their groups, then kill their babies to trigger estrus. As poaching declined, so did infanticide. "Now we have a high density of groups and low human disturbance," Stoinski says, "and infanticide is up because of increased intergroup interactions. It's fascinating to see how the gorillas react."

Perhaps one of the biggest surprises to park officials and Stoinski, who has published nearly a hundred papers on primate behavior and conservation, was the reappearance in January of a silverback presumed dead. Cantsbee, one of the last two gorillas named by Fossey, was the longest lived male recorded by researchers. He reigned over Pablo, Karisoke's largest group,

and according to an analysis that ended in 2013, fathered at least 28 babies—a record among studied gorillas. After the rufous-browed legend disappeared last October, at the age of 37, scores of trackers spent a fruitless month scouring the forest for his body. Finally, the Fossey Fund published an obituary, noting that he was born during a time of intense poaching but lived to a ripe age thanks to conservation measures.

Cantsbee's return upended many assumptions about dominant male behavior. "For a leader of his age and status to go and then come back— that's never been seen," Stoinski says, with a note of wonder. "Plus, he looked great—superfit."

In Cantsbee's absence his son Gicurasi had

become Pablo's leader; upon his return Cantsbee sometimes led the group but by no means dominated. Then, in February, looking weak, he slipped away for the last time. His body was found in May.

To Karisoke researchers, everything happening in the park today demonstrates how flexible mountain gorillas, like most big-brained primates, can be. In Fossey's time, groups under observation contained just two or three males. In the 1990s and early 2000s when human interference declined, groups grew considerably in size and had as many as eight silverbacks. More recently researchers have observed many group splits, often after the death of a dominant male, resulting

And so the Fossey Fund continues to monitor animals and help remove snares, even as it invests in social programs. The organization created a school library and computer center in Bisate, where it also built a maternity ward; it runs conservation education programs that reach about 13,000 Rwandans a year; and it plans to help villagers find ways to make a living that don't include scrambling over the park's stone wall.

Gorillas are already shifting into areas of the park with fewer groups. But humans may need to cede land to gorillas too. The government has proposed a buffer zone that would force people, their livestock, and their farm plots farther downhill. That would be enormously controversial, since 1,813 people per square mile call Musanze District home. "We need to make sure that the communities understand the value of the park," Stoinski says. After all, gorilla trekking is the mainstay of the nation's tourism industry, which brought in $367 million in 2015, and the park shares 10 percent of its revenue with local communities.

Watching a mother gorilla dandle a tiny puff of an infant while a pair of adolescents wrestle on a mattress of vines, it's easy to forget the human gymnastics that make such a delightful tableau possible. Critics ask whether these extreme conservation efforts consume money that might better be spent on other species, and some have suggested they may even disrupt natural selection by helping less fit individuals survive.

But Vecellio steadfastly defends the work. "We are keeping these gorillas alive, reversing the human impacts," she says, "because it's humans who have made them endangered." □

again in groups that look more like those of Fossey's time. "This shows us that behavior doesn't exist in a vacuum. It depends on a larger context," Stoinski says. "As their environment and circumstances change, so do things like gorilla social organization." And because gorillas take a long time to mature, it takes long-term studies to even hint at what "normal" means.

WHILE HUMAN ACTIVITIES are propelling about 60 percent of wild primate species toward extinction, one great ape population is rising. Even so, the mountain gorillas of the Virungas are still vulnerable. "The population is incredibly small and fragile," Stoinski warns.

Elizabeth Royte, a regular contributor, last visited Africa to write about the decline of vultures in the January 2016 issue. Ronan Donovan, who trained as a wildlife biologist, discovered a talent and passion for photography while researching chimpanzees in Uganda.

# Borderlands

## A visual meditation on the walls and fences that separate the United States and Mexico—and divide public opinion

STORY AND PHOTOGRAPHS
BY RICHARD MISRACH

A steel wall slices through farmland in Brownsville, Texas, north of the U.S.-Mexico border. Built inland of the actual border – the Rio Grande – it comes to an abrupt end, making it easy to circumvent on foot.

I have been working in the American Southwest for nearly 40 years. In 2004 I came across something I hadn't seen before: a blue barrel with a plain blue flag on a pole, with *"agua"* written on the side and several gallons of water inside. I photographed it because it was so unexpected, and it haunted me.

In 2009—as I became aware of an increase in the building of walls and surveillance towers and other government activities along the 1,954-mile-long U.S. border with Mexico—I began photographing in earnest. That's also when I discovered that the original barrel was a water station placed by a humanitarian group to help prevent the dehydration and death of migrants crossing the border.

The way I have always worked is by focusing on the landscape. Rarely do my images represent people, yet their passage is always felt. The presence of absence.

For this project I'd usually fly to a city and rent a four-by-four so I could explore the more remote regions of the border. Sometimes I'd set off a ground sensor, which brought out U.S. Border Patrol agents. Some were terrific—one even came out to protect me because she was worried that cartel activity was nearby—but others could be hostile.

People who don't live near the border may not realize that there's already a lot of wall in place—roughly 700 miles. It's expensive and laborious. You have to design it, fabricate it, pay eminent domain to landowners, then install it. One mile of wall has cost anywhere from $4 million to $12 million.

But how much good does it do? People can climb over it, tunnel under it, and—when it abruptly ends—walk around it.

Functionally speaking, a border wall attempts to do two things. One is to stem migration—people coming into this country for greater opportunity. But only when we stop hiring will they stop coming.

The other is to keep out drugs—but Americans are the ones creating the demand. Until we address the problem successfully on our end, the cartels will find ways to get through. A wall doesn't stop the reasons that this is happening.

It has been argued that the idea of national sovereignty—that the nation-state has impermeable borders—has already been broken, by everything from the Internet to global capitalism to viruses. Borders are collapsing on an existential level. To me the building of walls seems more symbolic than anything, a desperate gesture.

These images exist where politics, culture, and nature intersect. Although I don't have answers to these complex problems, I hope my work generates serious contemplation of the issues at hand. □

The humanitarian group Water Station put out this barrel of water — one of 160 containers placed throughout the desert regions of the California-Mexico border, where it can reach 120°F or higher. Volunteers of all political stripes monitor these spots every two weeks from spring to fall, checking for activity and refilling the water.

I assumed this fence near Los Indios, Texas, wasn't finished when I photographed it, but two years later nothing had changed. Today it functions more like a sculpture than a barrier. The caretaker of a playground (top right) in Gadsden, Arizona, says that the adjacent wall ruins the sunset. In the 19th century, obelisks called border monuments — like this one in Patagonia, Arizona (bottom right) — marked the divide.

In remote areas — like this stretch near Ocotillo, California — vehicle deterrents are made of railroad ties. They're often called Normandy barriers because they look like some of the blockades used during World War II. Border walls that are meant to keep out pedestrians are designed differently — solid or thinly slatted, standing 12 to 16 feet tall.

Richard Misrach's book *Border Cantos,* a collaboration with composer Guillermo Galindo, was published in 2016 by Aperture.

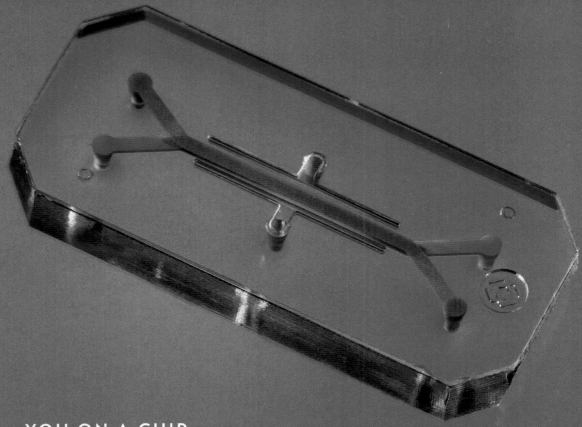

## YOU ON A CHIP

By Natasha Daly

Before, it was inconceivable: risk-free biomedical testing on living human organs. But new "organs-on-chips" technology is emulating the liver, brain, lungs, intestines, and more on a chip the size of a USB stick. Until now scientists conducted most biomedical research through animal testing—which often doesn't translate to humans—or in a petri dish, a static environment that doesn't let cells behave as if they are in the human body.

The organ-chip (above) consists of transparent channels lined with thousands of living cells and pumped with liquid containing nutrients, or blood, all interacting just as they would in the body. It's a "home away from home, a window into human biology," says Geraldine A. Hamilton, chief scientific officer of organ-chip developer Emulate, Inc. The chips have been used to test drugs' impact on organs and to replicate diseases like asthma.

The next frontier: custom chips that imitate a person's unique biology—or, as Hamilton puts it, "you on a chip."

ACTUAL
SIZE

15 mm

35 mm

Watch organ-chips in action at *ngm.com/Sep2017*.

# GET CLOSER
## TRAVEL WITH NATIONAL GEOGRAPHIC

## NATIONAL GEOGRAPHIC
# EXPEDITIONS

EXPERIENCE THE WORLD'S WONDERS WITH NATIONAL GEOGRAPHIC, FROM THE PANDAS OF SICHUAN, CHINA TO THE PALACES OF VENICE, ITALY. WITH OUR EXPERTS AND GUIDES, YOU CAN TRAVEL TO ALL SEVEN CONTINENTS ON TRIPS FOR PHOTOGRAPHERS, HIKERS, FAMILIES, WILDLIFE ENTHUSIASTS, TRAIN BUFFS, AND MORE. NO MATTER WHICH TRIP YOU CHOOSE, WE'LL GET YOU CLOSER THAN YOU EVER IMAGINED.

NATGEOEXPEDITIONS.COM | +1-202-835-0021

**Goldie's Bird
of Paradise**
(*Paradisaea decora*,
**Size:**
Body length, male
approx. 33 cm;
females approx.
29 cm
**Weight:**
Approx. 237 g
**Habitat:**
Secondary rainfores
and forest edges o
only two islands
**Surviving
number:**
Estimated at 650

*Photographed by
Tim Laman*

# WILDLIFE AS CANON SEES IT

The show must go on. Bobbing, jumping, calling "wok-wok," and displaying their vibrant plumes, mature male Goldie's birds of paradise put on a remarkable performance to capture the attention of potential female partners. Males display together in a hierarchical group, known as a "lek," using sites high up in the trees that they carefully maintain by plucking

incoming leaves. But it remains to be seen whether these brilliant birds will be able to go on, threatened as they are by loss and degradation of their forest habitat.

As Canon sees it, images have the power to raise awareness of the threats facing endangered species and the natural environment, helping us make the world a better place.

EOS System

# Canon